Houghton
Mifflin
Harcourt

© Houghton Mifflin Harcourt Publishing Company • Cover Image Credits: (Hares) ©Radius Images/Corbis; (Garden, New York) ©Rick Lew/The Image Bank/Getty Images; (sky) ©PhotoDisc/Getty Images

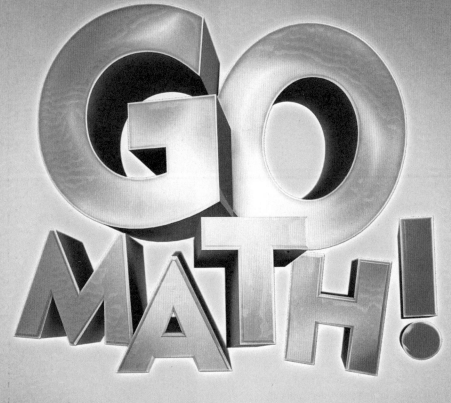

Volume 2

Made in the United States
Text printed on 100%
recycled paper

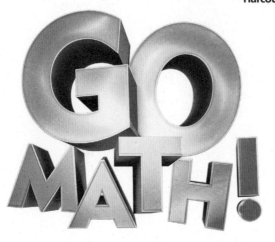

Houghton
Mifflin
Harcourt

2017 Edition

Copyright © by Houghton Mifflin Harcourt Publishing Company

Printed in the U.S.A.

ISBN 978-0-544-71053-5

12 13 14 15   0607   24 23 22 21

4500817327   D E F G

Dear Students and Families,

Welcome to **Go Math!**, Kindergarten! In this exciting mathematics program, there are hands-on activities to do and real-world problems to solve. Best of all, you will write your ideas and answers right in your book. In **Go Math!**, writing and drawing on the pages helps you think deeply about what you are learning, and you will really understand math!

By the way, all of the pages in your **Go Math!** book are made using recycled paper. We wanted you to know that you can Go Green with **Go Math!**

Sincerely,

The Authors

Made in the United States
Text printed on 100% recycled paper

GO MATH!

Authors

Juli K. Dixon, Ph.D.
Professor, Mathematics Education
University of Central Florida
Orlando, Florida

Edward B. Burger, Ph.D.
President, Southwestern University
Georgetown, Texas

Steven J. Leinwand
Principal Research Analyst
American Institutes for
    Research (AIR)
Washington, D.C.

Contributor

Rena Petrello
Professor, Mathematics
Moorpark College
Moorpark, CA

Matthew R. Larson, Ph.D.
K-12 Curriculum Specialist for
    Mathematics
Lincoln Public Schools
Lincoln, Nebraska

Martha E. Sandoval-Martinez
Math Instructor
El Camino College
Torrance, California

English Language Learners Consultant

Elizabeth Jiménez
CEO, GEMAS Consulting
Professional Expert on English
    Learner Education
Bilingual Education and
    Dual Language
Pomona, California

© Houghton Mifflin Harcourt Publishing Company • Image Credits: (bg) ©Russ Bishop/Alamy Images ; (t) ©Richard Wear/Design Pics/Corbis

VOLUME 1
Number and Operations

Big Idea Represent, count, write, order, and compare whole numbers to 20. Develop a conceptual understanding of addition and subtraction through 10. Count to 100 by ones and tens.

Vocabulary Reader Fall Festival! 1

GO DIGITAL

Go online! Your math lessons are interactive. Use *iTools*, Animated Math Models, the Multimedia *eGlossary*, and more.

① Represent, Count, and Write Numbers 0 to 5   **9**

✓ Show What You Know 10
   Vocabulary Builder 11
   Game: Bus Stop 12
 1 Hands On • Model and Count 1 and 2 13
 2 Count and Write 1 and 2 19
 3 Hands On • Model and Count 3 and 4 25
 4 Count and Write 3 and 4 31
✓ Mid-Chapter Checkpoint 34
 5 Hands On • Model and Count to 5 37
 6 Count and Write to 5 43
 7 Hands On: Algebra • Ways to Make 5 49
 8 Hands On • Count and Order to 5 55
 9 Problem Solving • Understand 0 61
10 Identify and Write 0. 67
✓ Chapter 1 Review/Test 73

Chapter 1 Overview

In this chapter, you will explore and discover answers to the following **Essential Questions**:

- How can you show, count, and write numbers?
- How can you show numbers 0 to 5?
- How can you count numbers 0 to 5?
- How can you write numbers 0 to 5?

② Compare Numbers to 5   **77**

✓ Show What You Know 78
   Vocabulary Builder 79
   Game: Counting to Blastoff 80
 1 Hands On • Same Number 81
 2 Hands On • Greater Than. 87
 3 Hands On • Less Than. 93
✓ Mid-Chapter Checkpoint 96
 4 Problem Solving • Compare by Matching Sets to 5. . . . 99
 5 Compare by Counting Sets to 5 105
✓ Chapter 2 Review/Test 111

Chapter 2 Overview

In this chapter, you will explore and discover answers to the following **Essential Questions**:

- How can building and comparing sets help you compare numbers?
- How does matching help you compare sets?
- How does counting help you compare sets?
- How do you know if the number of counters in one set is the same as, greater than, or less than the number of counters in another set?

In this chapter, you will explore and discover answers to the following **Essential Questions:**

- How can you show, count, and write numbers 6 to 9?
- How can you show numbers 6 to 9?
- How can you count numbers 6 to 9?
- How can you write numbers 6 to 9?

Practice and Homework

Lesson Check and Spiral Review in every lesson

3 Represent, Count, and Write Numbers 6 to 9   115

✓ Show What You Know 116
Vocabulary Builder 117
Game: Number Line Up 118
1 Hands On • Model and Count 6. 119
2 Count and Write to 6 125
3 Hands On • Model and Count 7. 131
4 Count and Write to 7 137
✓ Mid-Chapter Checkpoint 140
5 Hands On • Model and Count 8. 143
6 Count and Write to 8 149
7 Hands On • Model and Count 9. 155
8 Count and Write to 9 161
9 Problem Solving • Numbers to 9 167
✓ Chapter 3 Review/Test 173

© Houghton Mifflin Harcourt Publishing Company

Represent and Compare Numbers to 10 — 177

✓ Show What You Know 178
Vocabulary Builder 179
Game: Spin and Count! 180
1 Hands On • Model and Count 10 181
2 Count and Write to 10 187
3 Hands On: **Algebra** • Ways to Make 10. 193
4 Count and Order to 10 199
✓ Mid-Chapter Checkpoint 202
5 Problem Solving • Compare by Matching Sets to 10 . . . 205
6 Compare by Counting Sets to 10 211
7 Compare Two Numbers 217
✓ Chapter 4 Review/Test 223

Chapter 4 Overview

In this chapter, you will explore and discover answers to the following **Essential Questions**:

• How can you show and compare numbers to 10?
• How can you count forward to 10?
• How can you show numbers from 1 to 10?
• How can using models help you compare two numbers?

Addition — 227

✓ Show What You Know 228
Vocabulary Builder 229
Game: Pairs That Make 7 230
1 Addition: Add To 231
2 Hands On • Addition: Put Together 237
3 Problem Solving • Act Out Addition Problems 243
4 Hands On: **Algebra** • Model and Draw Addition Problems. 249
✓ Mid-Chapter Checkpoint 252
5 Algebra • Write Addition Sentences for 10 255
6 Algebra • Write Addition Sentences 261
7 Algebra • Write More Addition Sentences 267
8 Hands On: **Algebra** • Number Pairs to 5. 273
9 Hands On: **Algebra** • Number Pairs for 6 and 7. . . . 279
10 Hands On: **Algebra** • Number Pairs for 8 285
11 Hands On: **Algebra** • Number Pairs for 9 291
12 Hands On: **Algebra** • Number Pairs for 10. 297
✓ Chapter 5 Review/Test 303

Chapter 5 Overview

In this chapter, you will explore and discover answers to the following **Essential Questions**:

• How can you show addition?
• How can using objects or pictures help you show addition?
• How can you use numbers and symbols to show addition?

Personal Math Trainer
Online Assessment and Intervention

In this chapter, you will explore and discover answers to the following **Essential Questions**:

• How can you show subtraction?

• How can you use numbers and symbols to show a subtraction sentence?

• How can using objects and drawings help you solve word problems?

• How can acting it out help you solve subtraction word problems?

• How can using addition help you solve subtraction word problems?

Personal Math Trainer
Online Assessment and Intervention

6 Subtraction 307

✓ Show What You Know 308
Vocabulary Builder 309
Game: Spin for More 310
1 Subtraction: Take From 311
2 Hands On • Subtraction: Take Apart 317
3 Problem Solving • Act Out Subtraction Problems 323
4 Hands On: Algebra • Model and Draw
Subtraction Problems 329
✓ Mid-Chapter Checkpoint 332
5 Algebra • Write Subtraction Sentences 335
6 Algebra • Write More Subtraction Sentences 341
7 Hands On: Algebra • Addition and Subtraction 347
✓ Chapter 6 Review/Test 353

Sheep and Ducks

Represent, Count, and Write 11 to 19   357

✓ Show What You Know 358
  Vocabulary Builder 359
  Game: Sweet and Sour Path 360
1 Hands On • Model and Count 11 and 12 361
2 Count and Write 11 and 12 367
3 Hands On • Model and Count 13 and 14 373
4 Count and Write 13 and 14 379
5 Hands On • Model, Count, and Write 15 385
6 Problem Solving • Use Numbers to 15 391
✓ Mid-Chapter Checkpoint 394
7 Hands On • Model and Count 16 and 17 397
8 Count and Write 16 and 17 403
9 Hands On • Model and Count 18 and 19 409
10 Count and Write 18 and 19 415
✓ Chapter 7 Review/Test 421

Chapter 7 Overview

In this chapter, you will explore and discover answers to the following **Essential Questions**:

• How can you show, count, and write numbers 11 to 19?
• How can you show numbers 11 to 19?
• How can you read and write numbers 11 to 19?
• How can you show the teen numbers as 10 and some more?

Represent, Count, and Write 20 and Beyond   425

✓ Show What You Know 426
  Vocabulary Builder 427
  Game: Who Has More? 428
1 Hands On • Model and Count 20 429
2 Count and Write to 20 435
3 Count and Order to 20 441
4 Problem Solving • Compare Numbers to 20 447
✓ Mid-Chapter Checkpoint 450
5 Count to 50 by Ones 453
6 Count to 100 by Ones 459
7 Count to 100 by Tens 465
8 Count by Tens 471
✓ Chapter 8 Review/Test 477

Chapter 8 Overview

In this chapter, you will explore and discover answers to the following **Essential Questions**:

• How can you show, count, and write numbers to 20 and beyond?
• How can you show and write numbers to 20?
• How can you count numbers to 50 by ones?
• How can you count numbers to 100 by tens?

© Houghton Mifflin Harcourt Publishing Company

Big Idea

Chapter 9 Overview

In this chapter, you will explore and discover answers to the following **Essential Questions**:

- How can you identify, name, and describe two-dimensional shapes?

- How can knowing the parts of two-dimensional shapes help you join shapes?

- How can knowing the number of sides and vertices of two-dimensional shapes help you identify shapes?

Personal Math Trainer
Online Assessment and Intervention

VOLUME 2

Geometry and Positions

Big Idea Identify, name, and describe two- and three-dimensional shapes. Describe positions of objects in space.

Vocabulary Reader School Fun **481**

9 Identify and Describe Two-Dimensional Shapes   489

✓ Show What You Know 490
  Vocabulary Builder 491
  Game: Number Picture 492
 1 Identify and Name Circles 493
 2 Describe Circles 499
 3 Identify and Name Squares. 505
 4 Describe Squares 511
 5 Identify and Name Triangles 517
 6 Describe Triangles 523
✓ Mid-Chapter Checkpoint 526
 7 Identify and Name Rectangles 529
 8 Describe Rectangles 535
 9 Identify and Name Hexagons. 541
10 Describe Hexagons 547
11 Hands On: **Algebra • Compare**
   Two-Dimensional Shapes 553
12 Problem Solving • Draw to Join Shapes 559
✓ Chapter 9 Review/Test 565

Identify and Describe
Three-Dimensional Shapes 569

✓ Show What You Know 570
Vocabulary Builder 571
Game: Follow the Shapes 572
1 Hands On • Three-Dimensional Shapes 573
2 Hands On • Identify, Name, and Describe Spheres . . . 579
3 Hands On • Identify, Name, and Describe Cubes 585
4 Hands On • Identify, Name, and Describe Cylinders . . . 591
5 Hands On • Identify, Name, and Describe Cones . . . 597
✓ Mid-Chapter Checkpoint 600
6 Problem Solving • Two- and
Three-Dimensional Shapes 603
7 Hands On • Model Shapes 609
8 Above and Below 615
9 Beside and Next To 621
10 In Front Of and Behind 627
✓ Chapter 10 Review/Test 633

Chapter 10 Overview

In this chapter, you will explore and discover answers to the following **Essential Questions**:

• How can identifying and describing shapes help you sort them?
• How can you describe three-dimensional shapes?
• How can you sort three-dimensional shapes?

Practice and Homework

Lesson Check and Spiral Review in every lesson

Big Idea

GO DIGITAL

Go online! Your math lessons are interactive. Use *iTools*, Animated Math Models, the Multimedia *e*Glossary, and more.

Chapter 11 Overview

In this chapter, you will explore and discover answers to the following **Essential Questions**:

• How can comparing objects help you measure them?

• How can you compare the length of objects?

• How can you compare the height of objects?

• How can you compare the weight of objects?

Chapter 12 Overview

In this chapter, you will explore and discover answers to the following **Essential Questions**:

• How does sorting help you display information?

• How can you sort and classify objects by color?

• How can you sort and classify objects by shape?

• How can you sort and classify objects by size?

• How do you display information on a graph?

xii

Measurement and Data

Big Idea Develop a conceptual understanding of measurement and data. Classify and count by color, shape, and size.

Vocabulary Reader Plants All Around **637**

 Measurement   **645**

✓ Show What You Know 646
  Vocabulary Builder 647
  Game: Connecting Cube Challenge. 648
1 Hands On • Compare Lengths 649
2 Hands On • Compare Heights. 655
3 Problem Solving • Direct Comparison 661
✓ Mid-Chapter Checkpoint 664
4 Hands On • Compare Weights 667
5 Length, Height, and Weight. 673
✓ Chapter 11 Review/Test 679

Classify and Sort Data   **683**

✓ Show What You Know 684
  Vocabulary Builder 685
  Game: At the Farm 686
1 Hands On: Algebra • Classify and Count by Color 687
2 Hands On: Algebra • Classify and Count by Shape . . .693
3 Hands On: Algebra • Classify and Count by Size. 699
✓ Mid-Chapter Checkpoint 702
4 Hands On • Make a Concrete Graph 705
5 Problem Solving • Read a Graph 711
✓ Chapter 12 Review/Test 717

Science, Technology, Engineering, and Math (STEM) Activities   **STEM 1**

Picture Glossary **H1**
Index **H14**

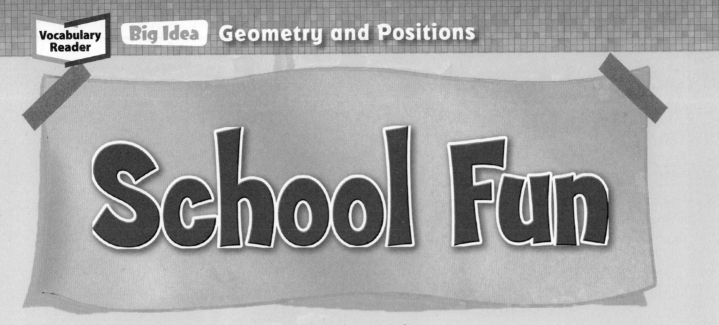

School Fun

written by Ann Dickson

BIG IDEA Identify, name, and describe two- and three-dimensional shapes. Describe positions of objects in space.

1. Sign in.

2. Put your book bag away.

3. Choose a center.

Here is my classroom. Come on in.

Learning time is about to begin.

Social Studies

Why do we have rules?

These are the book bags

we hang by our names.

Circle the ones that look the same.

Social Studies

Why do we need to take turns?

Here are the books. We read them all!

Which books are big?

Which books are small?

Social Studies

Why do we help others?

Here are markers of every kind.

Name all of the colors that you can find.

Social Studies

Why do we put things away?

Our blocks and toys are over there.

Which shapes are round?

Which shapes are square?

Why do we share?

Write About the Story

WRITE Math

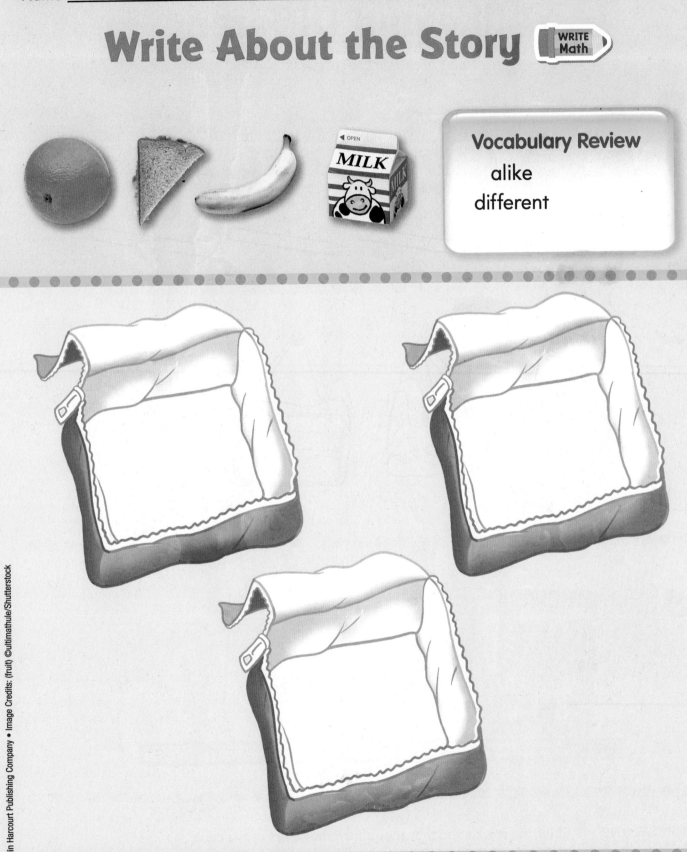

Vocabulary Review
alike
different

© Houghton Mifflin Harcourt Publishing Company • Image Credits: (fruit) ©ultimathule/Shutterstock

DIRECTIONS These lunch boxes are alike. In one lunch box draw something that you like to eat. Now circle the lunch box that is different.

Alike and Different

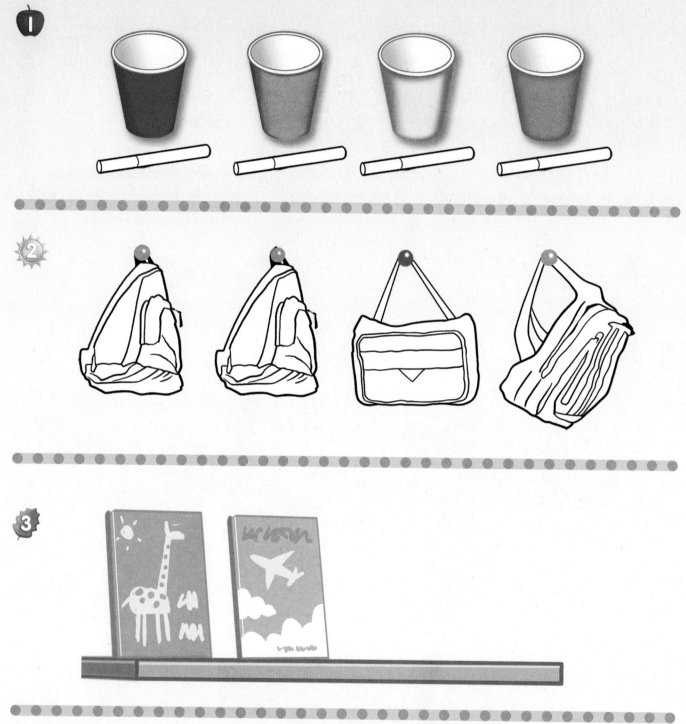

DIRECTIONS 1. Color the markers so that they match the colors of the cups.
2. Color the book bags that are alike by shape. 3. This classroom needs some
books. Draw a book that is a different size.

Identify and Describe Two-Dimensional Shapes

Chapter 9

Curious About Math with Curious George

The sails on these boats are shaped like a triangle.

- How many stripes can you count on the first sail?

✓ **Show What You Know**

Personal Math Trainer
Online Assessment
and Intervention

Shape

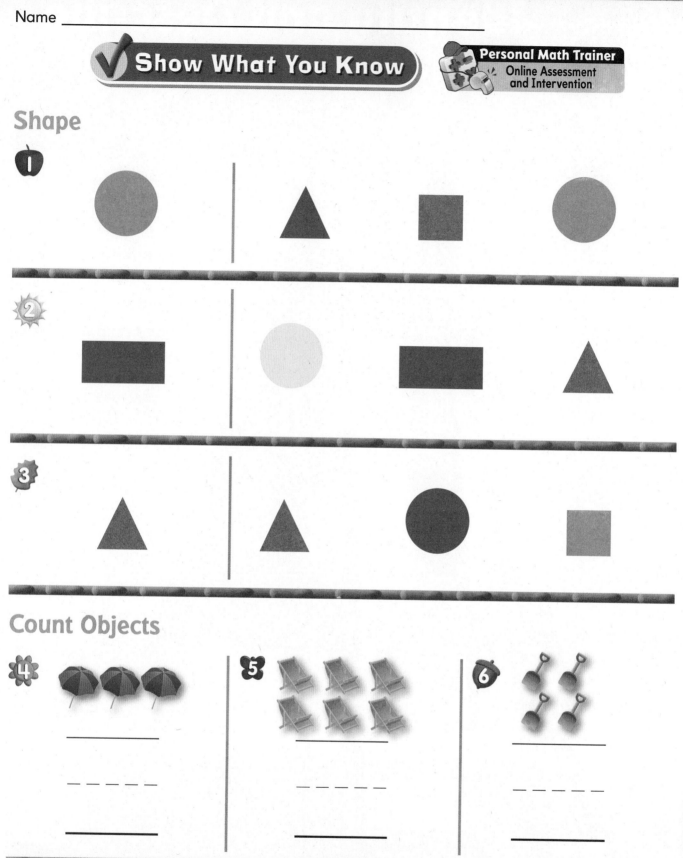

Count Objects

This page checks understanding of important skills needed for success in Chapter 9.

DIRECTIONS 1–3. Look at the shape at the beginning of the row. Mark an X on the shape that is alike. 4–6. Count and tell how many. Write the number.

Name _____

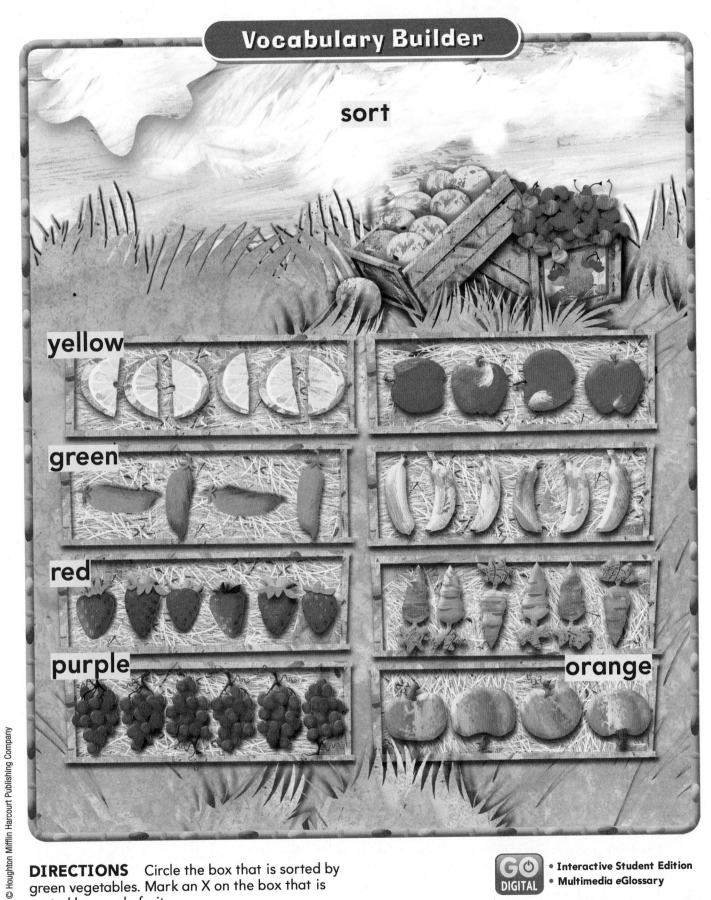

Vocabulary Builder

sort

yellow

green

red

purple   orange

DIRECTIONS Circle the box that is sorted by green vegetables. Mark an X on the box that is sorted by purple fruit.

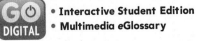

• Interactive Student Edition
• Multimedia *eGlossary*

Game Number Picture

DIRECTIONS Play with a partner. Decide who goes first. Toss the number cube. Color a shape in the picture that matches the number rolled. A player misses a turn if a number is rolled and all shapes with that number are colored. Continue until all shapes in the picture are colored.

MATERIALS number cube (labeled 1, 2, 2, 3, 3, 4), crayons

Chapter 9 Vocabulary

alike igual 3	**circle** círculo 11
curve curva 16	**different** diferente 19
hexagon hexágono 34	**rectangle** rectángulo 52
side lado 63	**square** cuadrado 70

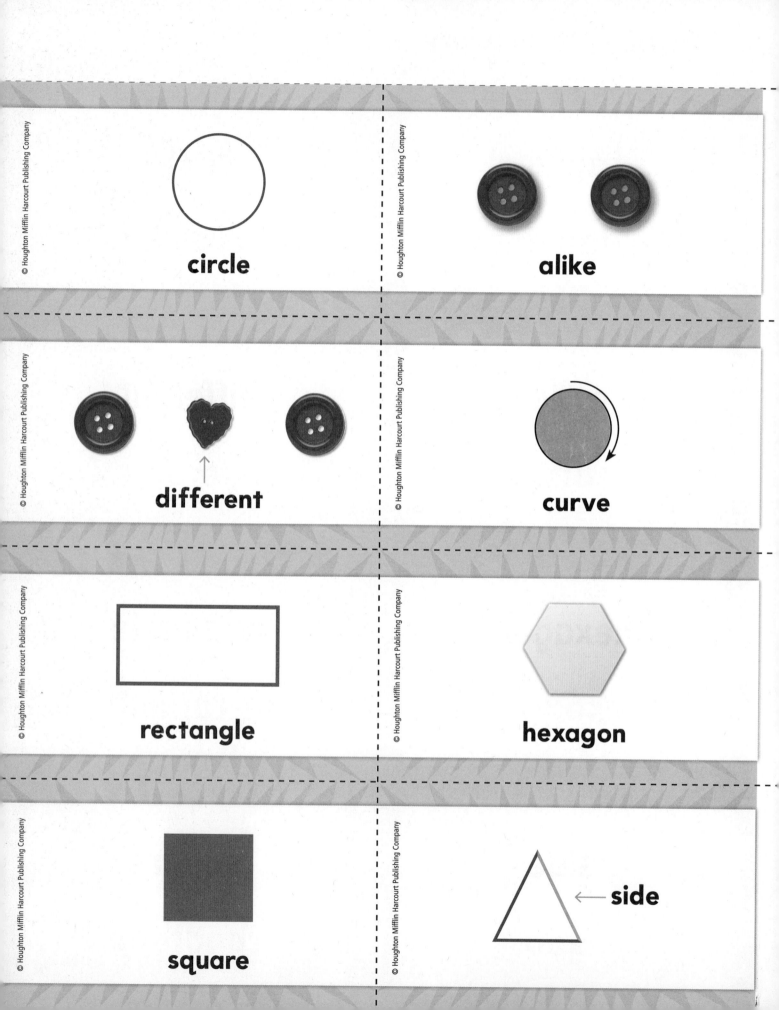

circle

alike

different

curve

rectangle

hexagon

square

side

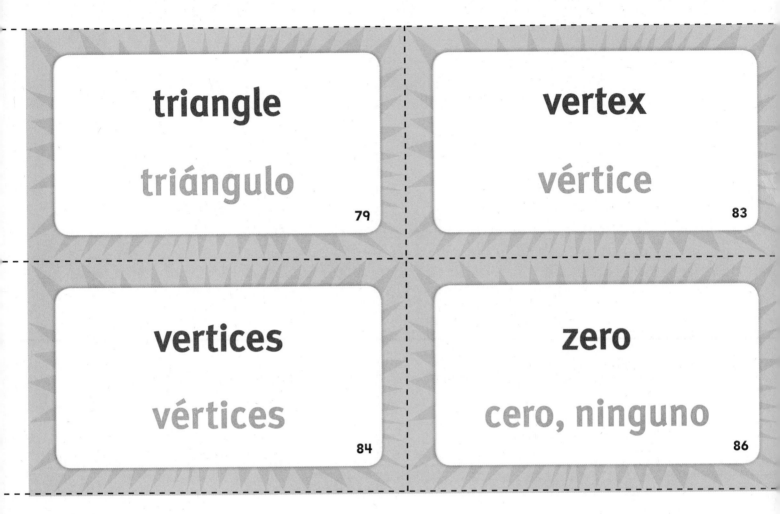

triangle

triángulo

79

vertex

vértice

83

vertices

vértices

84

zero

cero, ninguno

86

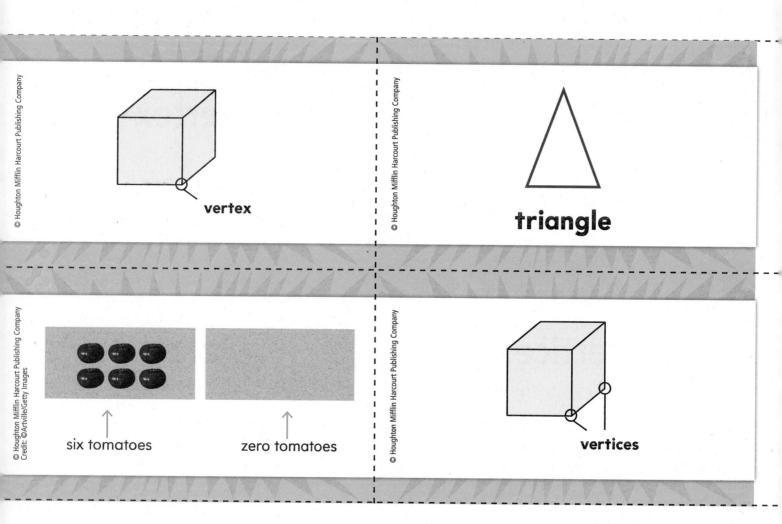

vertex

triangle

six tomatoes   zero tomatoes

vertices

Game

Shapes

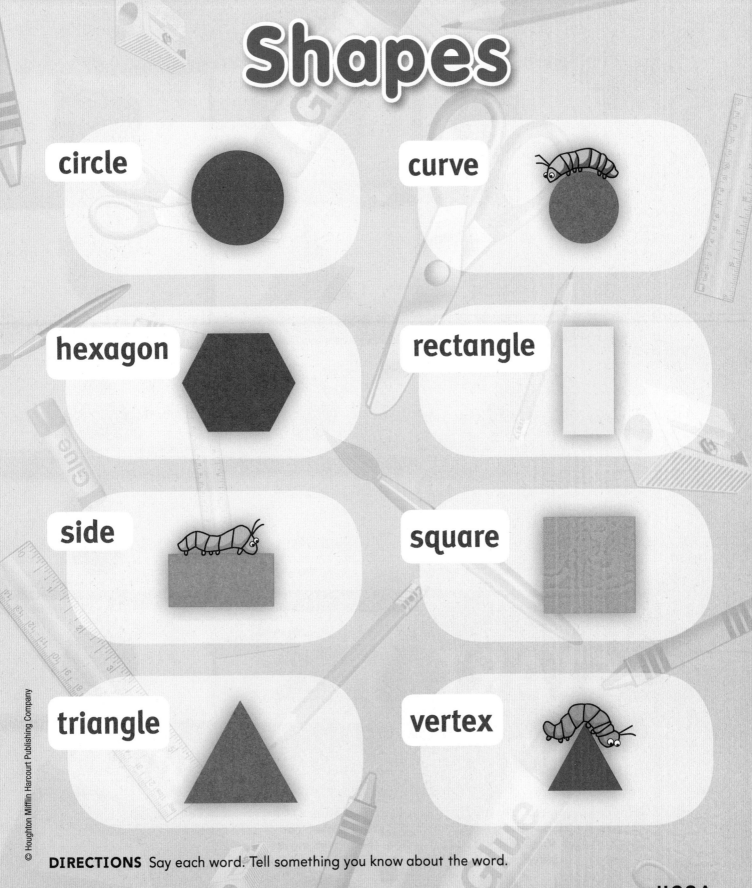

circle

curve

hexagon

rectangle

side

square

triangle

vertex

DIRECTIONS Say each word. Tell something you know about the word.

Game

START

DIRECTIONS Place game pieces on START. Play with a partner. Take turns. Toss the number cube. Move that many spaces. If a player can name the shape and tell something about the shape, the player moves ahead 1 space. The first player to reach FINISH wins.

MATERIALS I connecting cube game piece for each player, number cube

492B four hundred ninety-two

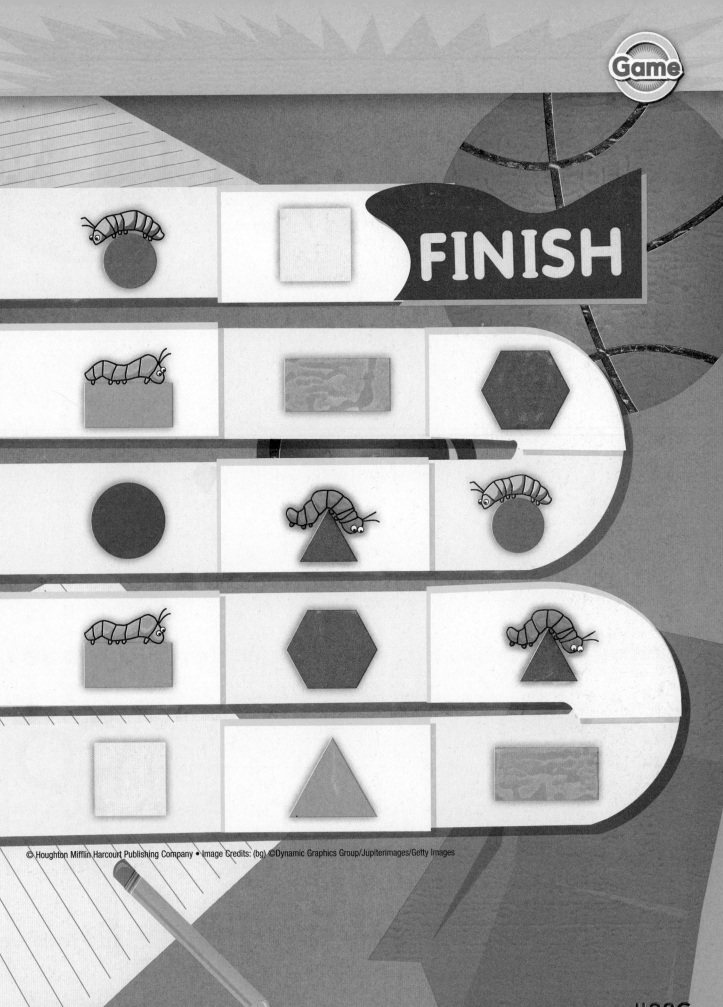

FINISH

The Write Way

DIRECTIONS Choose two shapes. Draw to show what you know about the shapes.
Reflect Be ready to tell about your drawing.

Name _____

Identify and Name Circles

Essential Question How can you identify and name circles?

Learning Objective You will identify and name circles.

Listen and Draw Real World Hands On

circles	not circles

DIRECTIONS Place two-dimensional shapes on the page. Identify and name the circles. Sort the shapes by circles and not circles. Trace and color the shapes on the sorting mat.

Chapter 9 • Lesson 1

four hundred ninety-three **493**

DIRECTIONS 1. Mark an X on all of the circles.

Name _____

DIRECTIONS 2. Color the circles in the picture.

Problem Solving • Applications Real World

3

4

DIRECTIONS 3. Neville puts his shapes in a row. Which shape is a circle? Mark an X on that shape. 4. Draw to show what you know about circles. Tell a friend about your drawing.

HOME ACTIVITY • Have your child show you an object that is shaped like a circle.

Name _____

Identify and Name Circles

Learning Objective You will identify and name circles.

DIRECTIONS **1.** Color the circles in the picture.

Chapter 9

four hundred ninety-seven **497**

Lesson Check

1

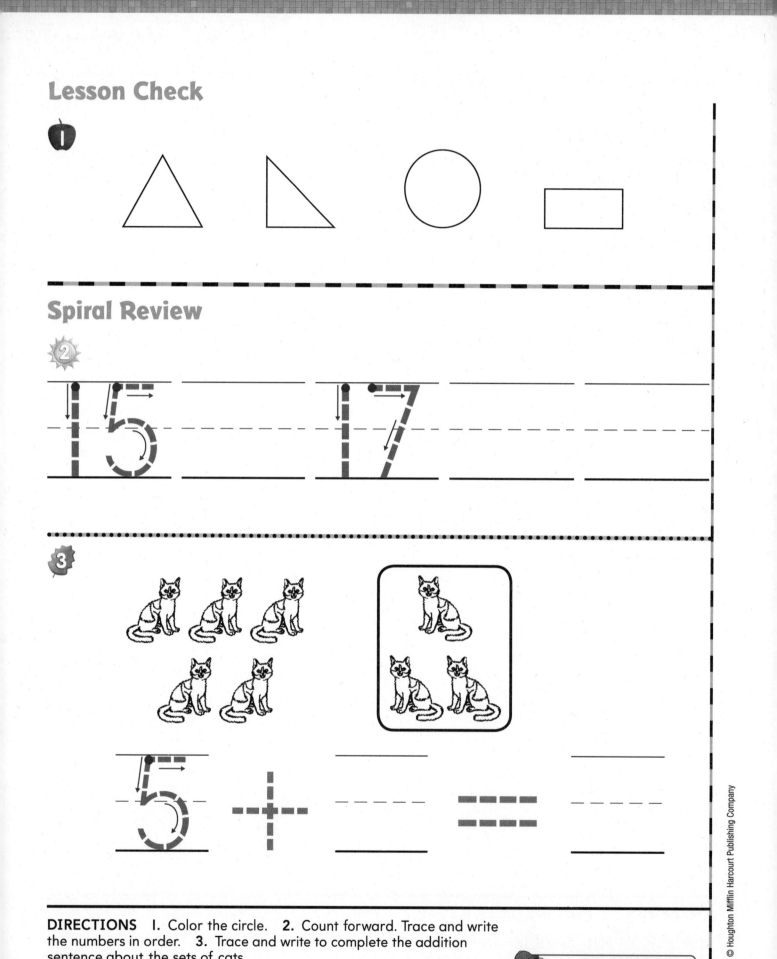

Spiral Review

2

15 17

3

5 + ___ = ___

DIRECTIONS 1. Color the circle. 2. Count forward. Trace and write the numbers in order. 3. Trace and write to complete the addition sentence about the sets of cats.

498 four hundred ninety-eight

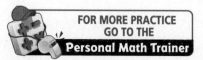

FOR MORE PRACTICE
GO TO THE
Personal Math Trainer

Name _____

Describe Circles

Essential Question How can you describe circles?

Learning Objective You will use informal language to describe the attributes of circles.

curve

DIRECTIONS Use your finger to trace around the circle. Talk about the curve. Trace around the curve.

four hundred ninety-nine **499**

1

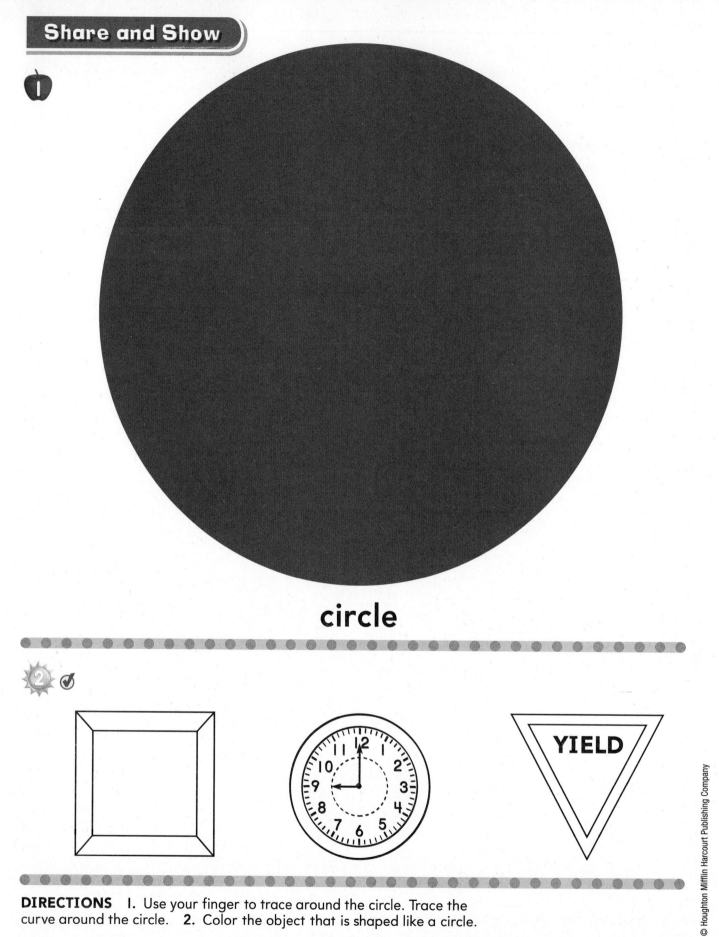

circle

2 ✓

DIRECTIONS 1. Use your finger to trace around the circle. Trace the curve around the circle. 2. Color the object that is shaped like a circle.

Name _____

3

DIRECTIONS 3. Use a pencil to hold one end of a large paper clip on one of the dots in the center of the page. Place another pencil in the other end of the paper clip. Move the pencil around to draw a circle.

Chapter 9 • Lesson 2

Problem Solving • Applications

4

WRITE Math

DIRECTIONS 4. I have a curve. What shape am I? Draw the shape. Tell a friend the name of the shape.

HOME ACTIVITY • Have your child describe a circle.

Name _____

Describe Circles

Learning Objective You will use informal language to describe the attributes of circles.

1

2

DIRECTIONS   I. Use a pencil to hold one end of a large paper clip on one of the dots in the center. Place another pencil in the other end of the paper clip. Move the pencil around to draw a circle.   **2.** Color the object that is shaped like a circle.

© Houghton Mifflin Harcourt Publishing Company

Chapter 9

Lesson Check

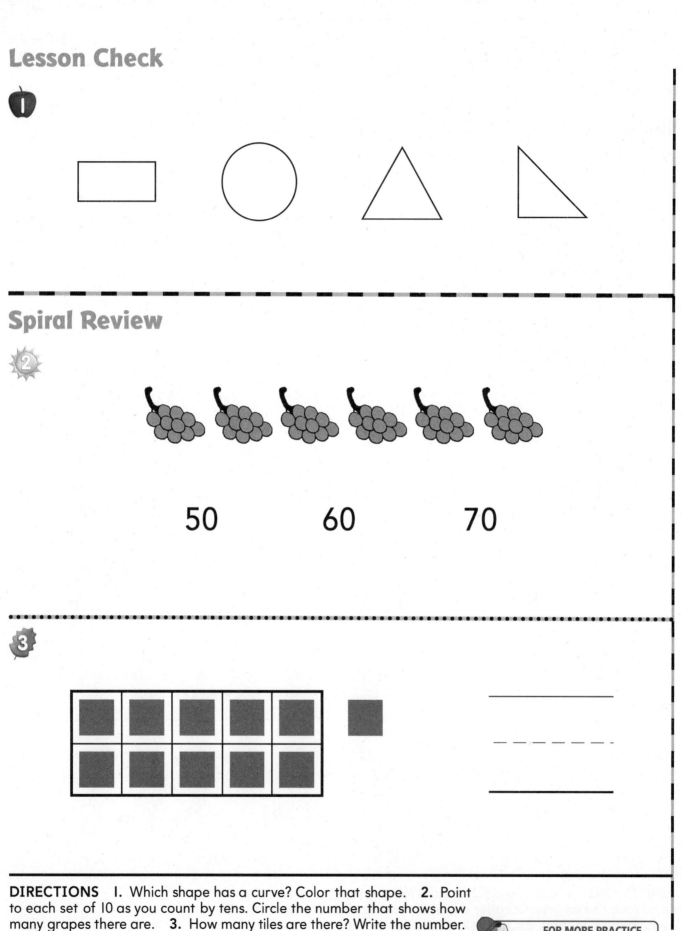

①

Spiral Review

②

50   60   70

③

DIRECTIONS **1.** Which shape has a curve? Color that shape. **2.** Point to each set of 10 as you count by tens. Circle the number that shows how many grapes there are. **3.** How many tiles are there? Write the number.

504 five hundred four

**FOR MORE PRACTICE
GO TO THE
Personal Math Trainer**

Name _____

Identify and Name Squares

Essential Question How can you identify and name squares?

Learning Objective You will identify and name squares.

squares	not squares

DIRECTIONS Place two-dimensional shapes on the page. Identify and name the squares. Sort the shapes by squares and not squares. Trace and color the shapes on the sorting mat.

Chapter 9 • Lesson 3

five hundred five **505**

1

⬤⬤⬤

DIRECTIONS 1. Mark an X on all of the squares.

Name _____

DIRECTIONS 2. Color the squares in the picture.

Chapter 9 • Lesson 3

five hundred seven **507**

Problem Solving • Applications Real World

3

WRITE Math

4

DIRECTIONS 3. Dennis drew these shapes. Which shapes are squares? Mark an X on those shapes. 4. Draw to show what you know about squares. Tell a friend about your drawing.

HOME ACTIVITY • Have your child show you an object that is shaped like a square.

508 five hundred eight

Name _____

Identify and Name Squares

Learning Objective You will identify and name squares.

1

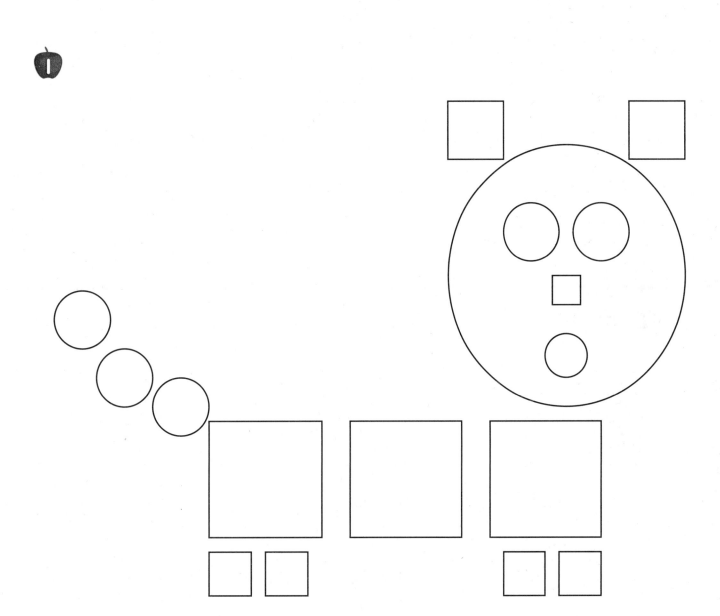

DIRECTIONS 1. Color the squares in the picture.

Chapter 9

five hundred nine **509**

Lesson Check

1

△   □   ○   ▭

Spiral Review

2

_____

_ _ _ _ _ _ _ _ _ _

_____

3

2 and 2 ___

DIRECTIONS 1. Which shape is a square? Color the square. **2.** How many tiles are there? Write the number. **3.** Trace the number of puppies. Trace the number of puppies being added. Write the number that shows how many puppies there are now.

510 five hundred ten

FOR MORE PRACTICE GO TO THE Personal Math Trainer

Name _____

Describe Squares

Essential Question How can you describe squares?

Learning Objective You will use informal language to describe the attributes of squares.

Listen and Draw

vertex

side

© Houghton Mifflin Harcourt Publishing Company

DIRECTIONS Use your finger to trace around the square. Talk about the number of sides and the number of vertices. Draw an arrow pointing to another vertex. Trace around the sides.

Chapter 9 • Lesson 4

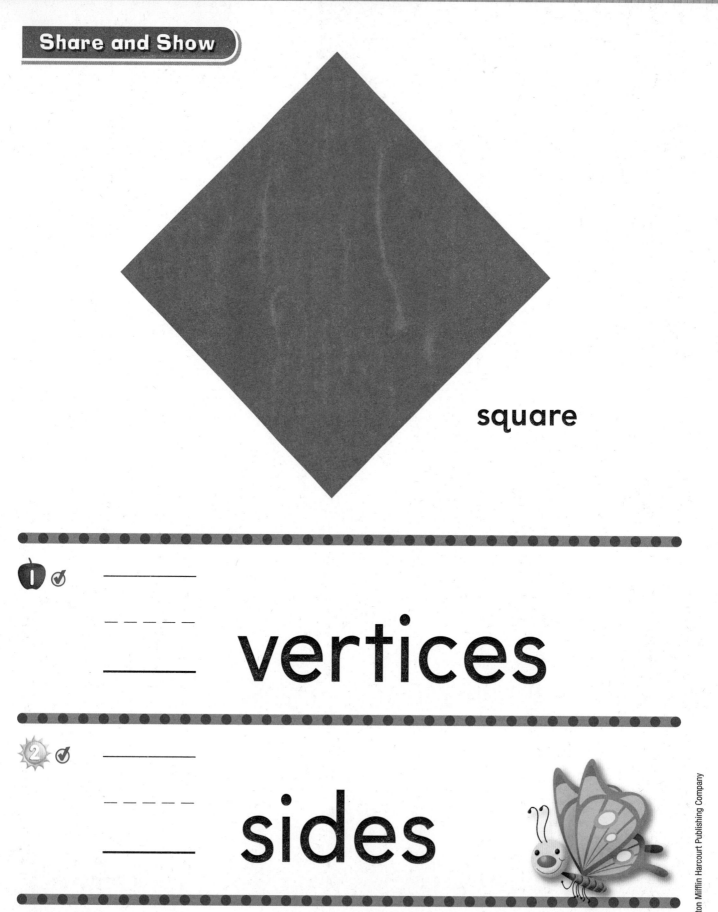

square

1 ⊘ _____

____ vertices

2 ⊘ _____

____ sides

DIRECTIONS 1. Place a counter on each corner, or vertex. Write how many corners, or vertices. 2. Trace around the sides. Write how many sides.

Name _____

3

DIRECTIONS 3. Draw and color a square.

Problem Solving • Applications

**WRITE
Math**

4

DIRECTIONS 4. I have 4 sides of equal length and 4 vertices. What shape am I? Draw the shape. Tell a friend the name of the shape.

HOME ACTIVITY • Have your child describe a square.

514   five hundred fourteen

Describe Squares

Learning Objective You will use informal language to describe the attributes of squares.

1
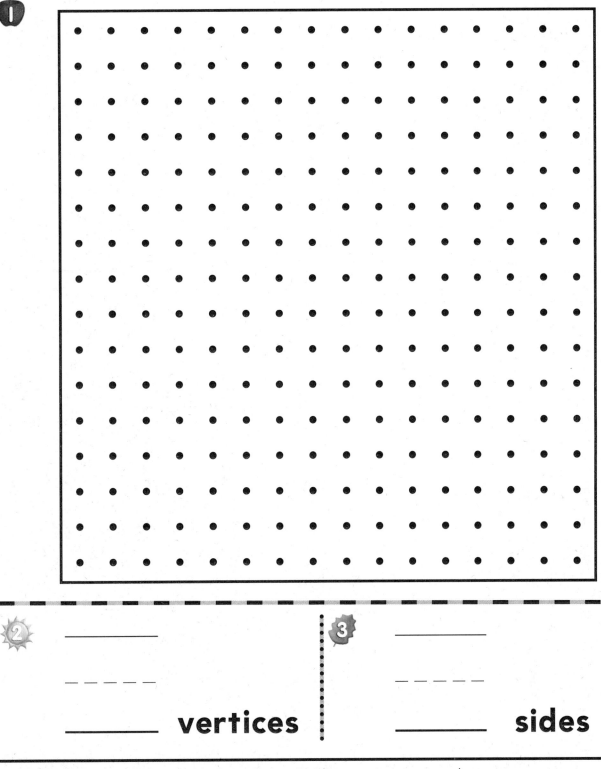

2 _____
_ _ _ _ _ _ _
_____ **vertices**

3 _____
_ _ _ _ _ _ _
_____ **sides**

DIRECTIONS 1. Draw and color a square. 2. Place a counter on each corner, or vertex, of the square that you drew. Write how many corners, or vertices. 3. Trace around the sides of the square that you drew. Write how many sides.

Lesson Check

_____

- - - - - - - - - -

_____ **vertices**

Spiral Review

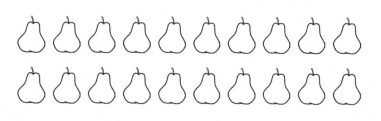

_____

- - - - - - - - - -

_____

3

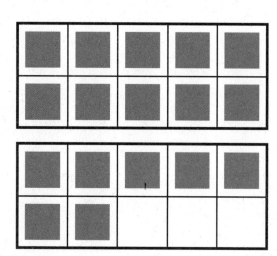

_____

- - - - - - - - - -

_____

DIRECTIONS **1.** How many vertices does the square have? Write the number. **2.** Count and tell how many pieces of fruit. Write the number. **3.** How many tiles are there? Write the number.

516 five hundred sixteen

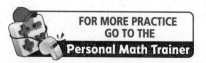

FOR MORE PRACTICE
GO TO THE
Personal Math Trainer

© Houghton Mifflin Harcourt Publishing Company

Name _____

Identify and Name Triangles

Essential Question How can you identify and name triangles?

Learning Objective You will identify and name triangles.

Listen and Draw Real World Hands On

triangles	not triangles

DIRECTIONS Place two-dimensional shapes on the page. Identify and name the triangles. Sort the shapes by triangles and not triangles. Trace and color the shapes on the sorting mat.

Chapter 9 • Lesson 5

1

DIRECTIONS 1. Mark an X on all of the triangles.

Name _____

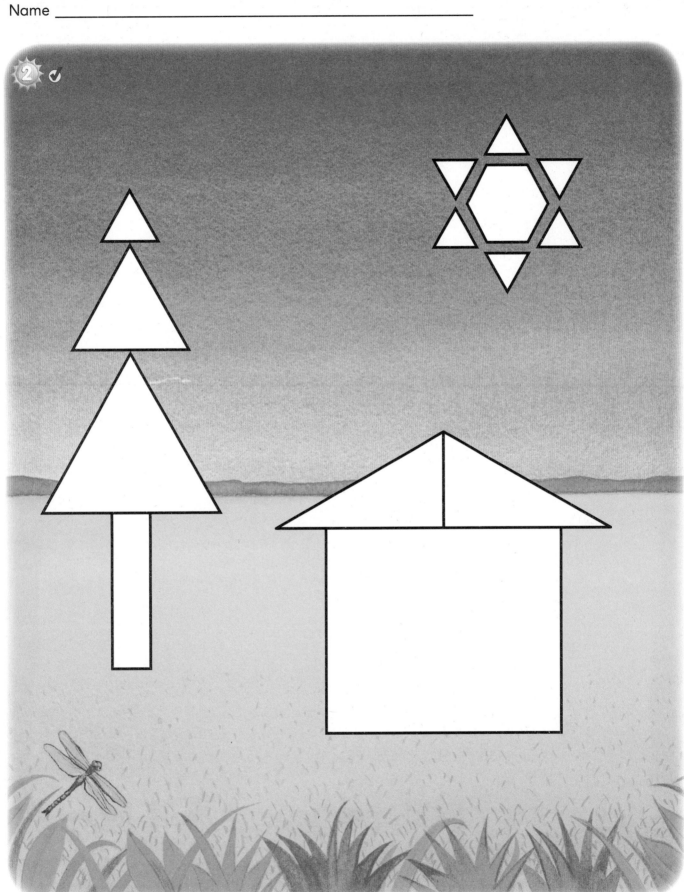

DIRECTIONS 2. Color the triangles in the picture.

Problem Solving • Applications   Real World

WRITE Math

3

4

DIRECTIONS   **3.** Anita put her shapes in a row. Which shapes are triangles? Mark an X on those shapes.   **4.** Draw to show what you know about triangles. Tell a friend about your drawing.

HOME ACTIVITY • Have your child show you an object that is shaped like a triangle.

520   five hundred twenty

Name _____

Identify and Name Triangles

Learning Objective You will identify and name triangles.

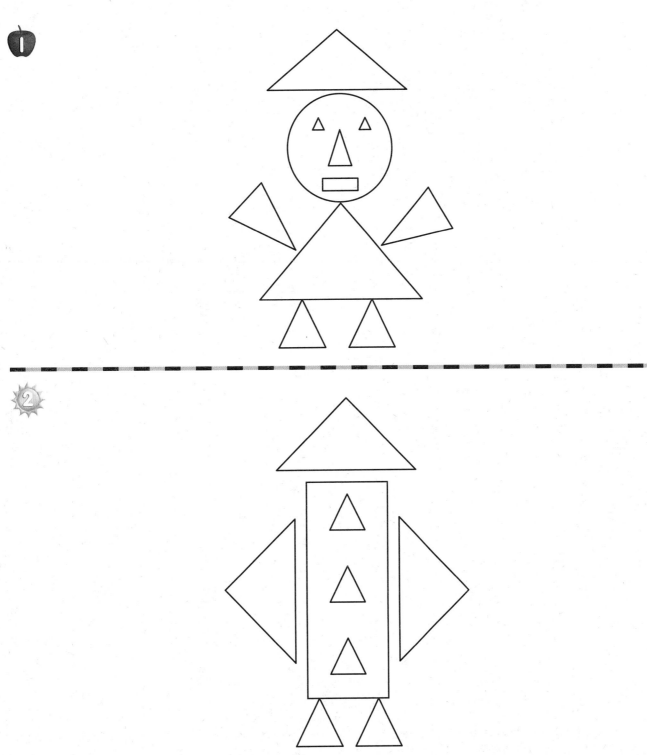

DIRECTIONS 1–2. Color the triangles in the picture.

Chapter 9

five hundred twenty-one **521**

Lesson Check

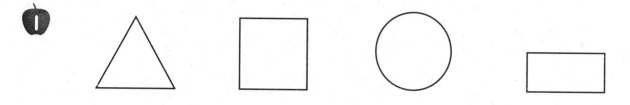

Spiral Review

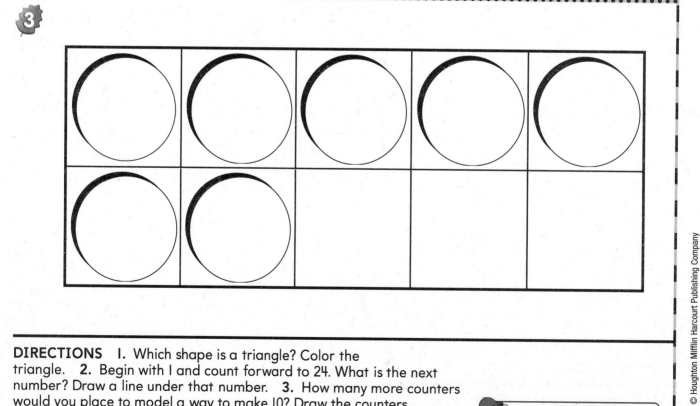

DIRECTIONS **1.** Which shape is a triangle? Color the triangle. **2.** Begin with 1 and count forward to 24. What is the next number? Draw a line under that number. **3.** How many more counters would you place to model a way to make 10? Draw the counters.

522 five hundred twenty-two

FOR MORE PRACTICE
GO TO THE
Personal Math Trainer

Name _____

Describe Triangles

Essential Question How can you describe triangles?

Learning Objective You will use informal language to describe the attributes of triangles.

Listen and Draw

vertex

side

© Houghton Mifflin Harcourt Publishing Company

DIRECTIONS Use your finger to trace around the triangle. Talk about the number of sides and the number of vertices. Draw an arrow pointing to another vertex. Trace around the sides.

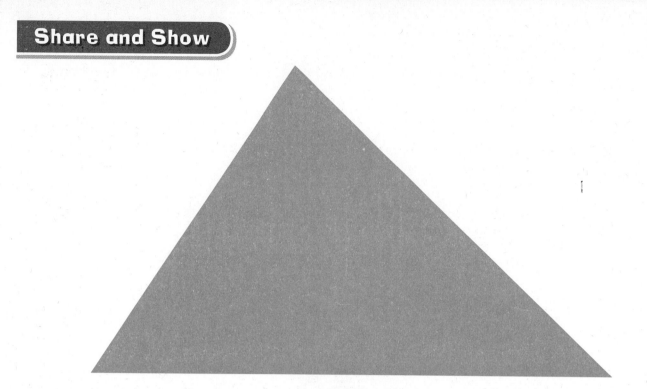

triangle

1 ✓ _____

_____ vertices

2 ✓ _____

_____ sides

DIRECTIONS 1. Place a counter on each corner, or vertex. Write how many corners, or vertices. 2. Trace around the sides. Write how many sides.

Name _____

3

DIRECTIONS 3. Draw and color a triangle.

HOME ACTIVITY • Have your child describe a triangle.

Personal Math Trainer
Online Assessment
and Intervention

Concepts and Skills

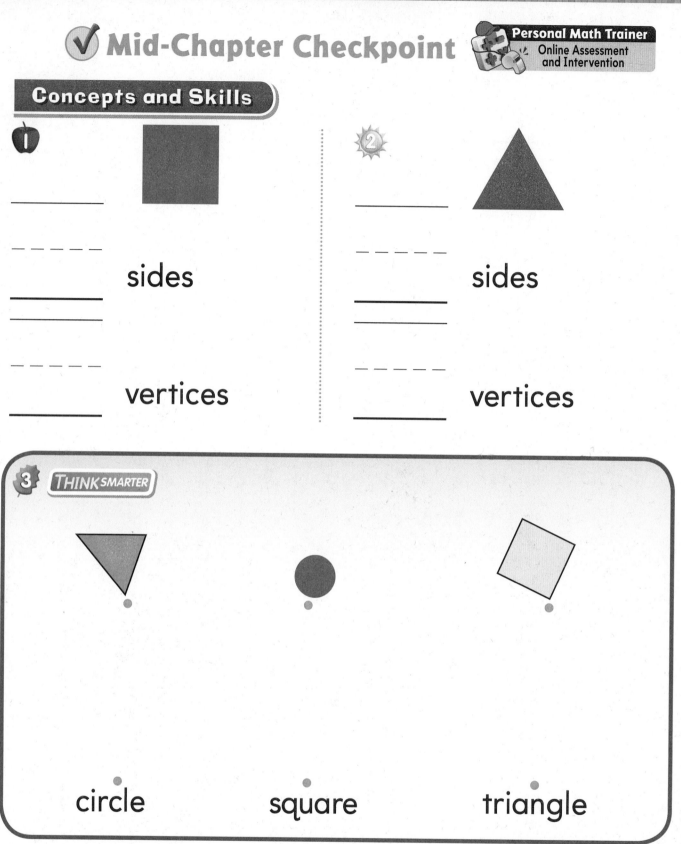

1.

_____ sides

_____ vertices

2.

_____ sides

_____ vertices

3. **THINK** SMARTER

circle   square   triangle

DIRECTIONS 1–2. Trace around each side. Write how many sides. Place a counter on each corner or vertex. Write how many vertices. **3.** Draw lines to match the shape to its name.

Name _____

Describe Triangles

Learning Objective You will use informal language to describe the attributes of triangles.

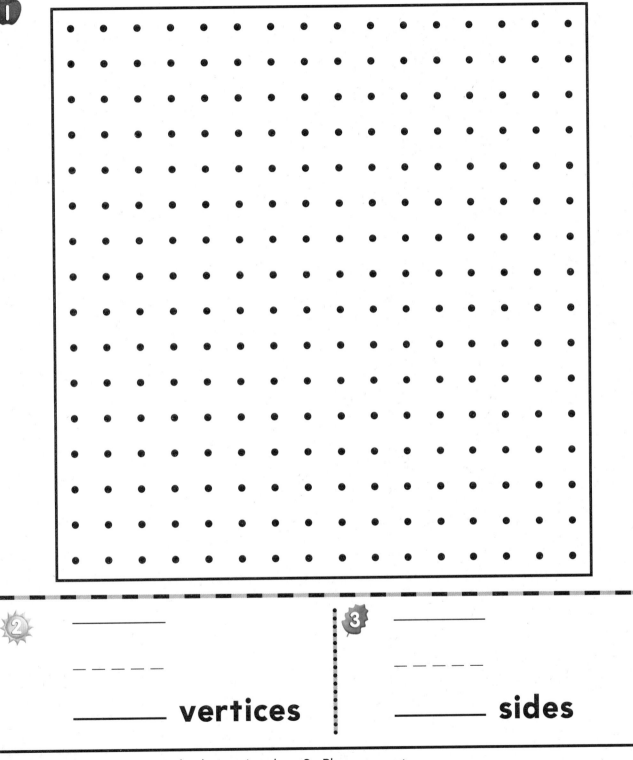

2 _____
_ _ _ _ _
_____ **vertices**

3 _____
_ _ _ _ _
_____ **sides**

DIRECTIONS **1.** Draw and color a triangle. **2.** Place a counter on each corner, or vertex, of the triangle that you drew. Write how many corners, or vertices. **3.** Trace around the sides of the triangle that you drew. Write how many sides.

Chapter 9

five hundred twenty-seven **527**

Lesson Check

1

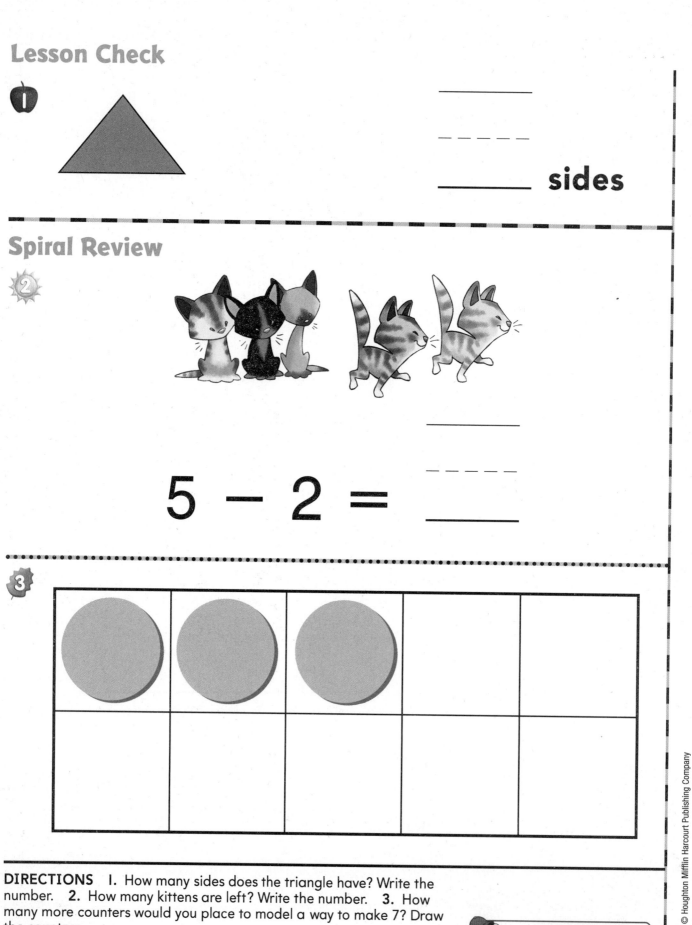

_____
- - - - - - - - - - - -
_____ **sides**

Spiral Review

2

$$5 - 2 = \underline{\qquad}$$

_____
- - - - - - - - - - - -

3

DIRECTIONS **1.** How many sides does the triangle have? Write the number. **2.** How many kittens are left? Write the number. **3.** How many more counters would you place to model a way to make 7? Draw the counters.

528 five hundred twenty-eight

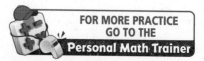

FOR MORE PRACTICE
GO TO THE
Personal Math Trainer

© Houghton Mifflin Harcourt Publishing Company

Name _____

Identify and Name Rectangles

Essential Question How can you identify and name rectangles?

Learning Objective You will identify and name rectangles.

Listen and Draw Real World

 Hands On

rectangles	not rectangles

DIRECTIONS Place two-dimensional shapes on the page. Identify and name the rectangles. Sort the shapes by rectangles and not rectangles. Trace and color the shapes on the sorting mat.

Chapter 9 • Lesson 7

Name _____

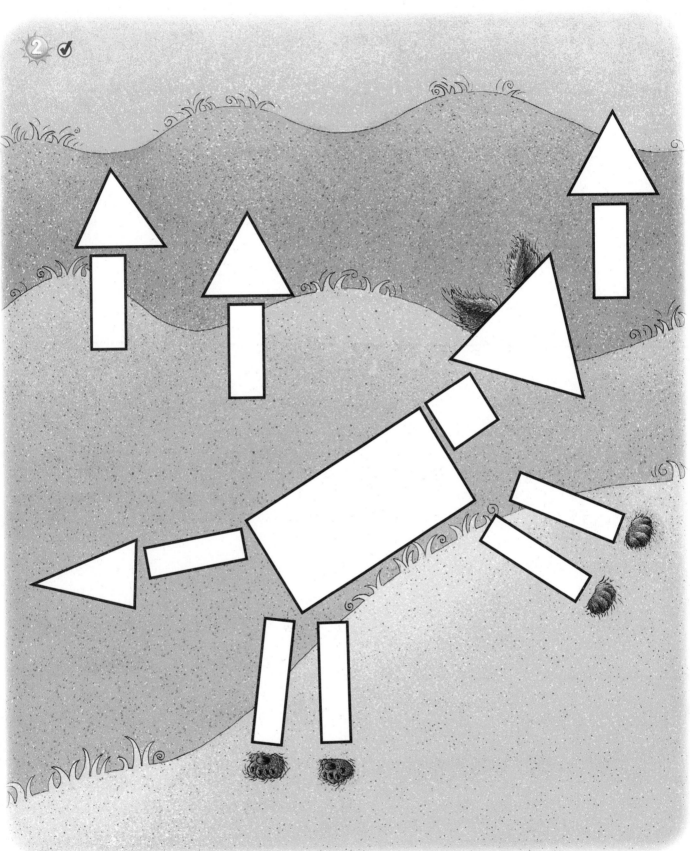

DIRECTIONS 2. Color the rectangles in the picture.

Problem Solving • Applications

3

WRITE Math

4

DIRECTIONS **3.** Max looked at his shapes. Which of his shapes are rectangles? Mark an X on those shapes. **4.** Draw to show what you know about rectangles. Tell a friend about your drawing.

HOME ACTIVITY • Have your child show you an object that is shaped like a rectangle.

Identify and Name Rectangles

Learning Objective You will identify and name rectangles.

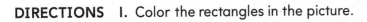

DIRECTIONS 1. Color the rectangles in the picture.

Chapter 9

five hundred thirty-three **533**

Lesson Check

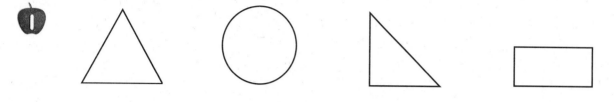

Spiral Review

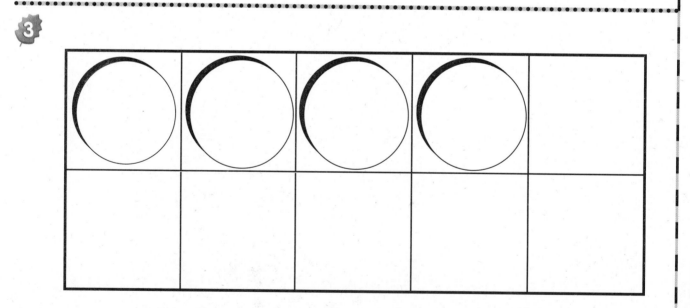

1	2	3	4	5	6	7	8	9	10
11	12	13	14	15	16	17	18	19	20
21	22	23	24	25	26	27	28	29	30

DIRECTIONS 1. Which shape is a rectangle? Color the rectangle.
2. Count by tens as you point to the numbers in the shaded boxes. Start
with the number 10. What number do you end with? Draw a line under
that number.   3. How many more counters would you place to model a
way to make 6? Draw the counters.

534 five hundred thirty-four

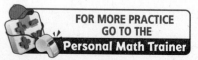

FOR MORE PRACTICE
GO TO THE
Personal Math Trainer

Name _____

Describe Rectangles

Essential Question How can you describe rectangles?

Learning Objective You will use informal language to describe the attributes of rectangles.

Listen and Draw

side

vertex

DIRECTIONS Use your finger to trace around the rectangle. Talk about the number of sides and the number of vertices. Draw an arrow pointing to another vertex. Trace around the sides.

Chapter 9 • Lesson 8

five hundred thirty-five **535**

rectangle

1 ✓ _____

_____ vertices

2 ✓ _____

_____ sides

DIRECTIONS 1. Place a counter on each corner, or vertex.
Write how many corners, or vertices. 2. Trace around the sides.
Write how many sides.

Name _____

3

DIRECTIONS 3. Draw and color a rectangle.

Problem Solving • Applications

4

WRITE
Math

DIRECTIONS 4. I have 4 sides and 4 vertices. What shape am I? Draw the shape. Tell a friend the name of the shape.

HOME ACTIVITY • Have your child describe a rectangle.

Name _____

Describe Rectangles

Learning Objective You will use informal language to describe the attributes of rectangles.

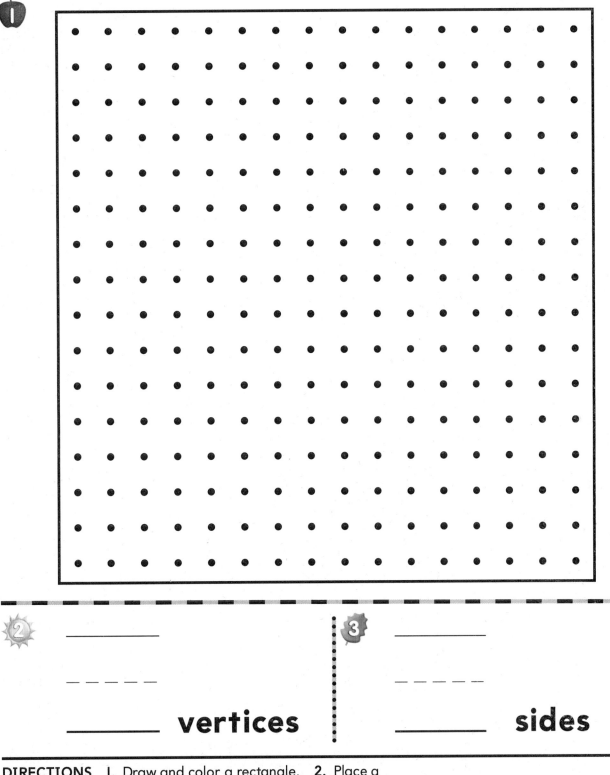

2 _____
_ _ _ _ _
_____ **vertices**

3 _____
_ _ _ _ _
_____ **sides**

DIRECTIONS I. Draw and color a rectangle. **2.** Place a counter on each corner, or vertex, of the rectangle that you drew. Write how many corners, or vertices. **3.** Trace around the sides of the rectangle that you drew. Write how many sides.

Chapter 9

Lesson Check

1

_____
- - - - - -
_____ **sides**

Spiral Review

2

_____   _____   _____

- - - - - **+** - - - - - **=** - - - - -

_____   _____   _____

3

_____
- - - - - -
_____

DIRECTIONS I. How many sides does the rectangle have? Write the number. **2.** Complete the addition sentence to show the numbers that match the cube train. **3.** Draw a set that has 20 connecting cubes. Write the number.

540 five hundred forty

FOR MORE PRACTICE
GO TO THE
Personal Math Trainer

Name _____

Identify and Name Hexagons

Essential Question How can you identify and name hexagons?

Learning Objective You will identify and name hexagons.

Listen and Draw Real World

hexagons	not hexagons

DIRECTIONS Place two-dimensional shapes on the page. Identify and name the hexagons. Sort the shapes by hexagons and not hexagons. Trace and color the shapes on the sorting mat.

DIRECTIONS 1. Mark an X on all of the hexagons.

DIRECTIONS 2. Color the hexagons in the picture.

Problem Solving • Applications Real World

3 WRITE Math

4

DIRECTIONS 3. Ryan is looking at his shapes. Which of his shapes are hexagons? Mark an X on those shapes. **4.** Draw to show what you know about hexagons. Tell a friend about your drawing.

HOME ACTIVITY • Draw some shapes on a page. Include several hexagons. Have your child circle the hexagons.

Identify and Name Hexagons

Learning Objective You will identify and name hexagons.

1

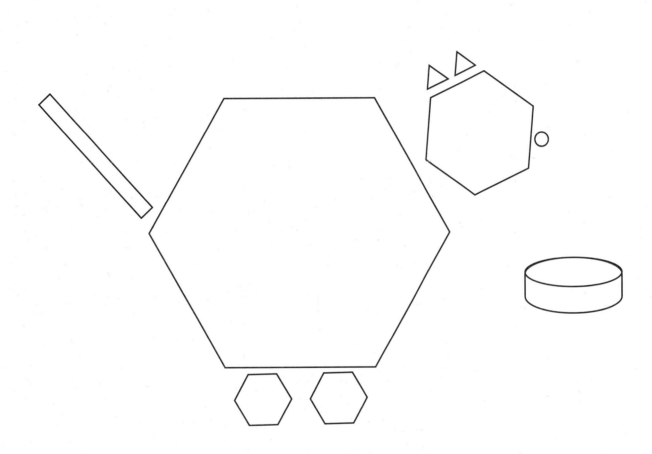

DIRECTIONS 1. Color the hexagons in the picture.

Lesson Check

Spiral Review

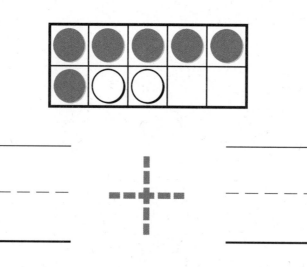

71	72	73	74	75	76	77	78	79	80
81	82	83	84	85	86	87	88	89	90
91	92	93	94	95	96	97	98	99	100

DIRECTIONS **1.** Which shape is a hexagon? Color the hexagon.
2. Begin with 81 and count forward to 90. What is the next number?
Draw a line under that number.   **3.** What numbers show the sets that
are put together? Write the numbers and trace the symbol.

546 five hundred forty-six

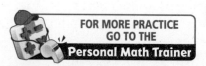

FOR MORE PRACTICE
GO TO THE
Personal Math Trainer

Name _____

Describe Hexagons

Essential Question How can you describe hexagons?

Learning Objective You will use informal language to describe the attributes of hexagons.

Listen and Draw

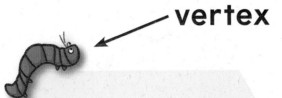

vertex

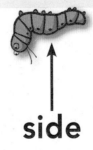

side

DIRECTIONS Use your finger to trace around the hexagon. Talk about the number of sides and the number of vertices. Draw an arrow pointing to another vertex. Trace around the sides.

Chapter 9 • Lesson 10

five hundred forty-seven **547**

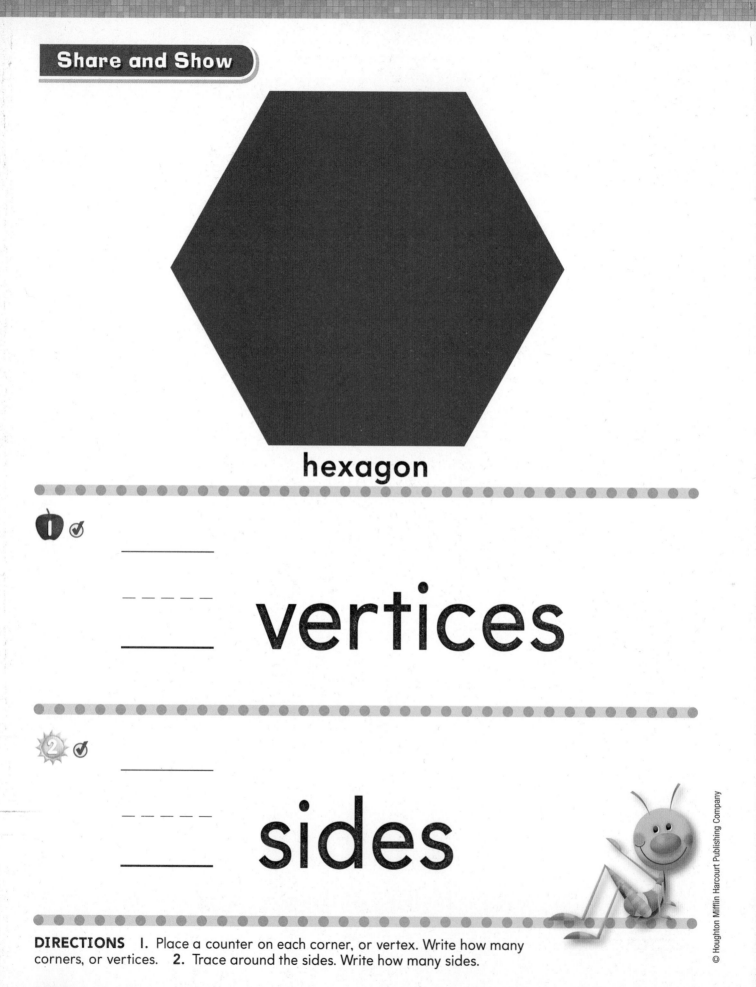

hexagon

① ✓

_____ vertices

② ✓

_____ sides

DIRECTIONS 1. Place a counter on each corner, or vertex. Write how many corners, or vertices. 2. Trace around the sides. Write how many sides.

Name _____

DIRECTIONS 3. Draw and color a hexagon.

Problem Solving • Applications

4.

WRITE Math

DIRECTIONS 4. I have 6 sides and 6 vertices. What shape am I? Draw the shape. Tell a friend the name of the shape.

HOME ACTIVITY • Have your child describe a hexagon.

Describe Hexagons

Learning Objective You will use informal language to describe the attributes of hexagons.

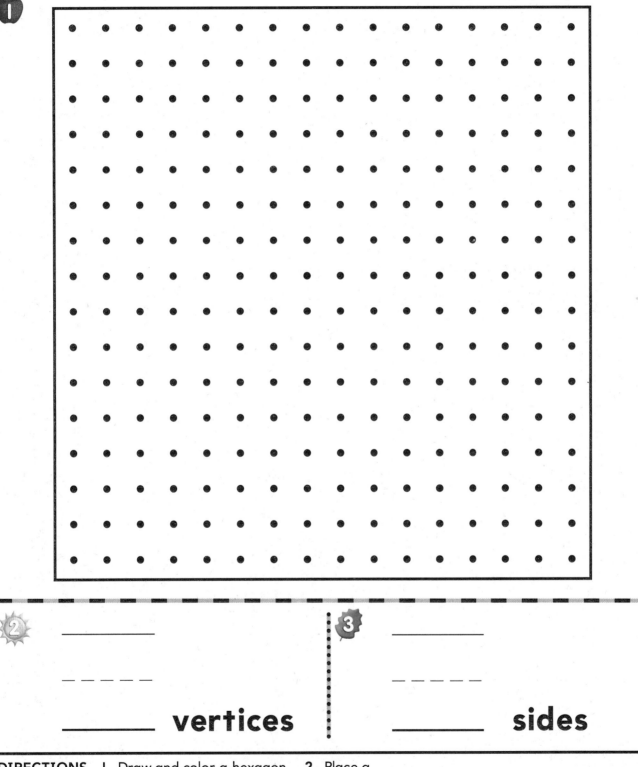

2 _____
_ _ _ _ _

_____ **vertices**

3 _____
_ _ _ _ _

_____ **sides**

DIRECTIONS 1. Draw and color a hexagon. 2. Place a counter on each corner, or vertex, of the hexagon that you drew. Write how many corners, or vertices. 3. Trace around the sides of the hexagon that you drew. Write how many sides.

Lesson Check

1

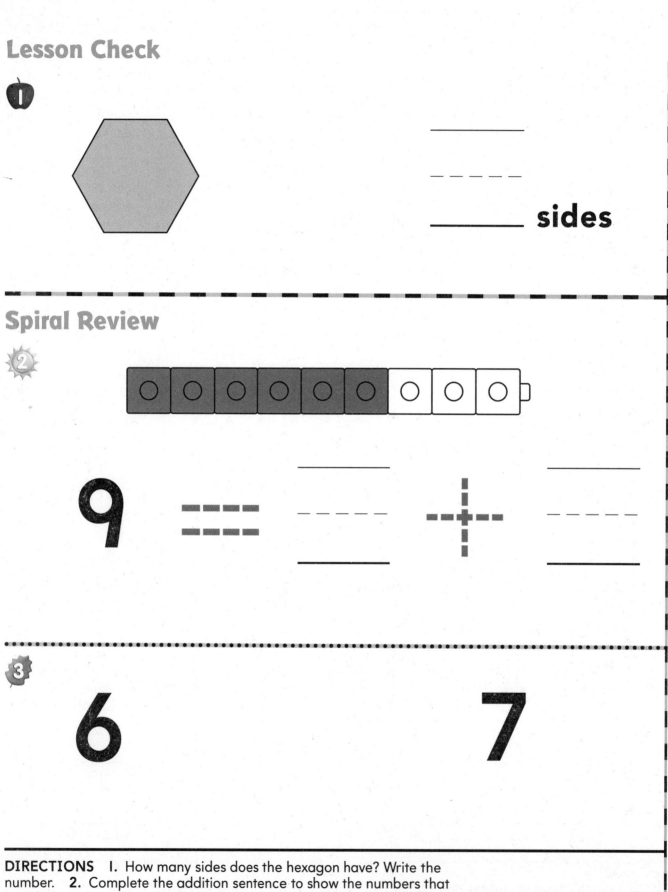

_____
- - - - - -
_____ **sides**

Spiral Review

2

9 = = = _____ - - - - - $+$ _____ - - - - -

3

6 7

DIRECTIONS 1. How many sides does the hexagon have? Write the number. 2. Complete the addition sentence to show the numbers that match the cube train. 3. Compare the numbers. Circle the number that is greater.

**FOR MORE PRACTICE
GO TO THE
Personal Math Trainer**

Name _____

Algebra • Compare Two-Dimensional Shapes

Essential Question How can you use the words *alike* and *different* to compare two-dimensional shapes?

Learning Objective You will use the words alike and different to compare two-dimensional shapes.

Listen and Draw

DIRECTIONS Look at the worms and the shapes. Use the words *alike* and *different* to compare the shapes. Use green to color the shapes with four vertices and four sides. Use blue to color the shapes with curves. Use red to color the shapes with three vertices and three sides.

© Houghton Mifflin Harcourt Publishing Company

1

alike	different

DIRECTIONS 1. Place two-dimensional shapes on the page. Sort the shapes by the number of vertices. Draw the shapes on the sorting mat. Use the words *alike* and *different* to tell how you sorted the shapes.

Name _____

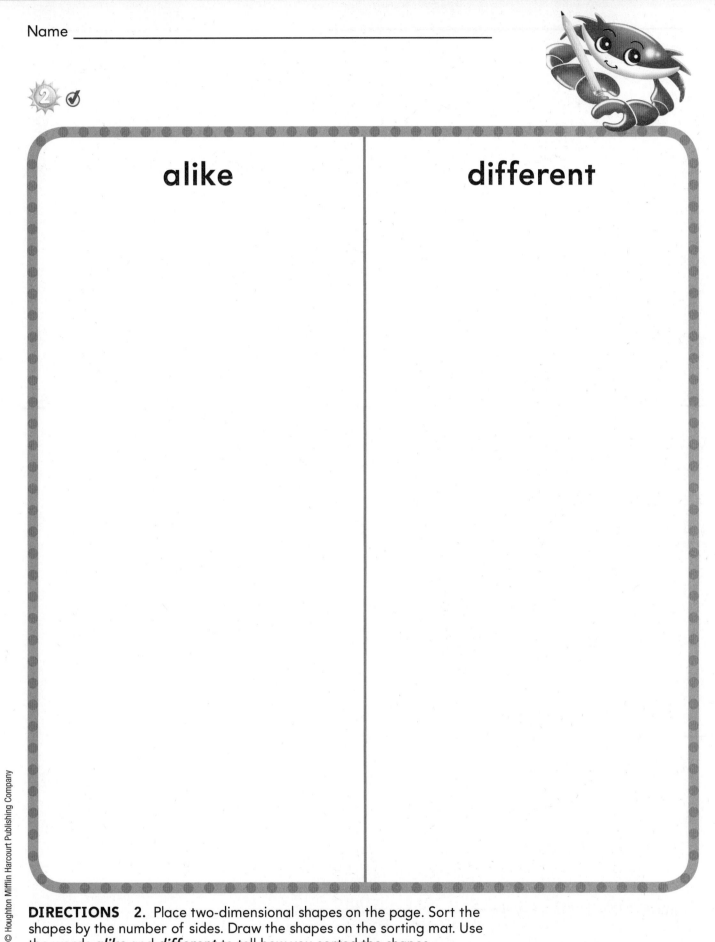

alike	different

DIRECTIONS 2. Place two-dimensional shapes on the page. Sort the shapes by the number of sides. Draw the shapes on the sorting mat. Use the words *alike* and *different* to tell how you sorted the shapes.

© Houghton Mifflin Harcourt Publishing Company

Chapter 9 • Lesson 11

Problem Solving • Applications

3 WRITE Math

4 | curve | no curve

DIRECTIONS 3. I have a curve. What shape am I? Draw the shape. 4. Draw to show shapes sorted by curves and no curves.

HOME ACTIVITY • Describe a shape and ask your child to name the shape that you are describing.

Algebra • Compare
Two-Dimensional Shapes

Learning Objective You will use the words alike and different to compare two-dimensional shapes.

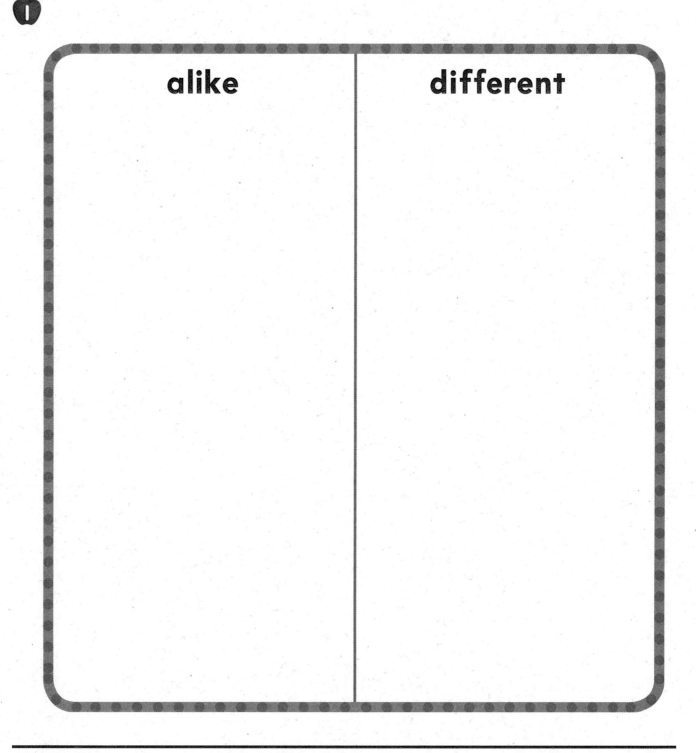

alike	different

© Houghton Mifflin Harcourt Publishing Company

DIRECTIONS   **1.** Place two-dimensional shapes on the page. Sort the shapes by the number of sides. Draw the shapes on the sorting mat. Use the words *alike* and *different* to tell how you sorted the shapes.

Lesson Check

1

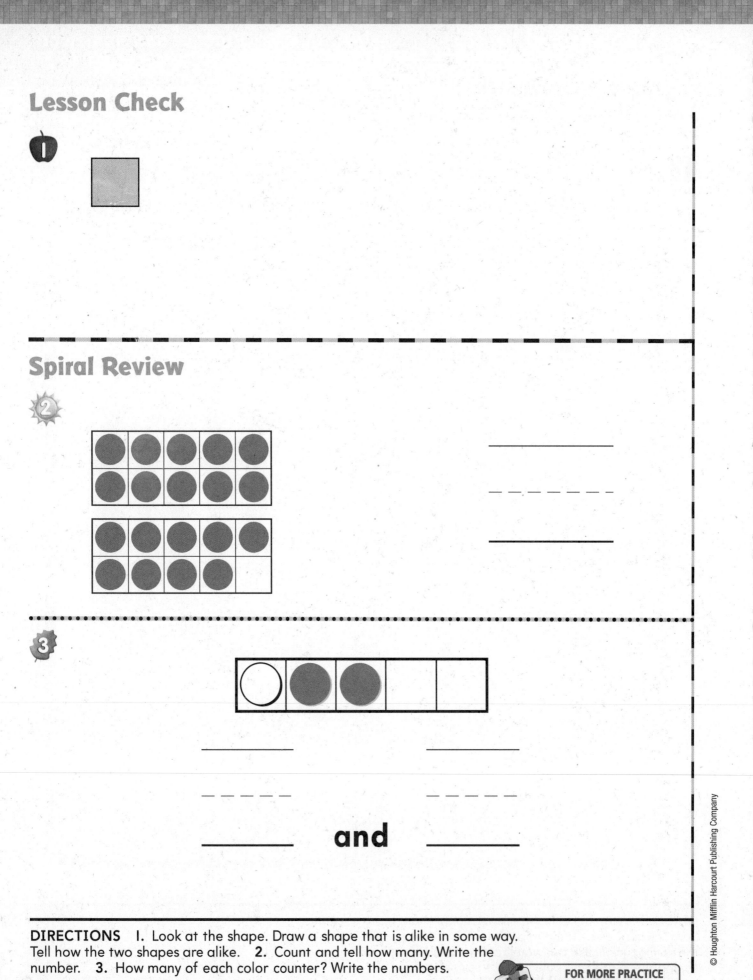

Spiral Review

2

_____

- - - - - - - - - - - - -

_____

3

_____   _____

- - - - - -   - - - - - -

_____ **and** _____

© Houghton Mifflin Harcourt Publishing Company

DIRECTIONS 1. Look at the shape. Draw a shape that is alike in some way. Tell how the two shapes are alike. **2.** Count and tell how many. Write the number. **3.** How many of each color counter? Write the numbers.

FOR MORE PRACTICE
GO TO THE
Personal Math Trainer

Name _____

Problem Solving • Draw to Join Shapes

Essential Question How can you solve problems using the strategy *draw a picture*?

Learning Objective You will use the strategy *draw a picture* by joining shapes to make new shapes to solve problems.

Unlock the Problem

Hands On

DIRECTIONS How can you join triangles to make the shapes? Draw and color the triangles.

© Houghton Mifflin Harcourt Publishing Company

Try Another Problem

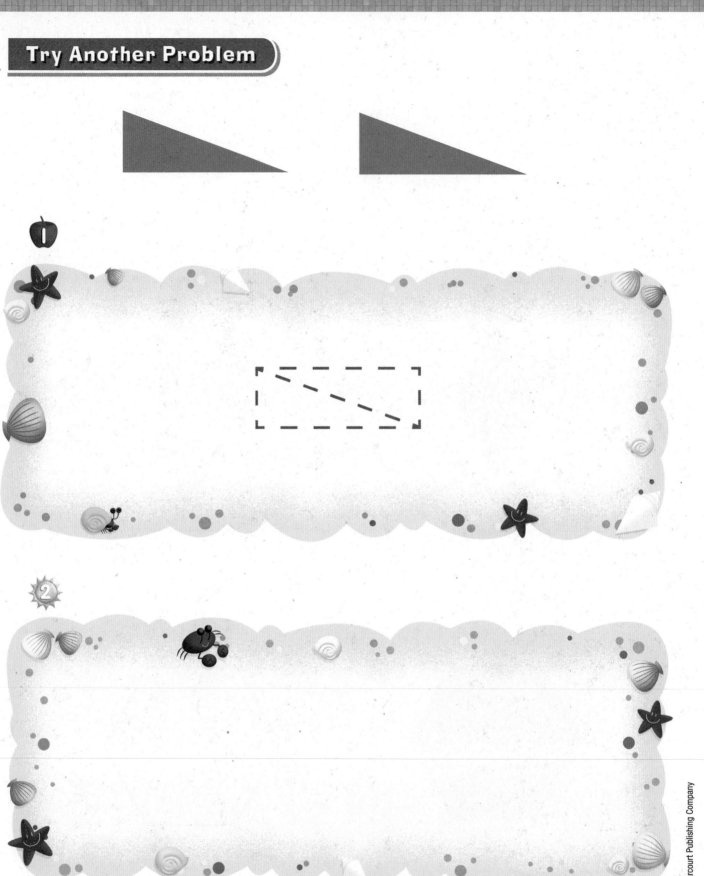

1

2

© Houghton Mifflin Harcourt Publishing Company

DIRECTIONS **1.** How can you join the two triangles to make a rectangle? Trace around the triangles to draw the rectangle. **2.** How can you join the two triangles to make a larger triangle? Use the triangle shapes to draw a larger triangle.

Name _____

③

④ ✓

DIRECTIONS 3. How can you join some of the squares to make a larger square? Use the square shapes to draw a larger square. 4. How can you join some or all of the squares to make a rectangle? Use the square shapes to draw a rectangle.

On Your Own

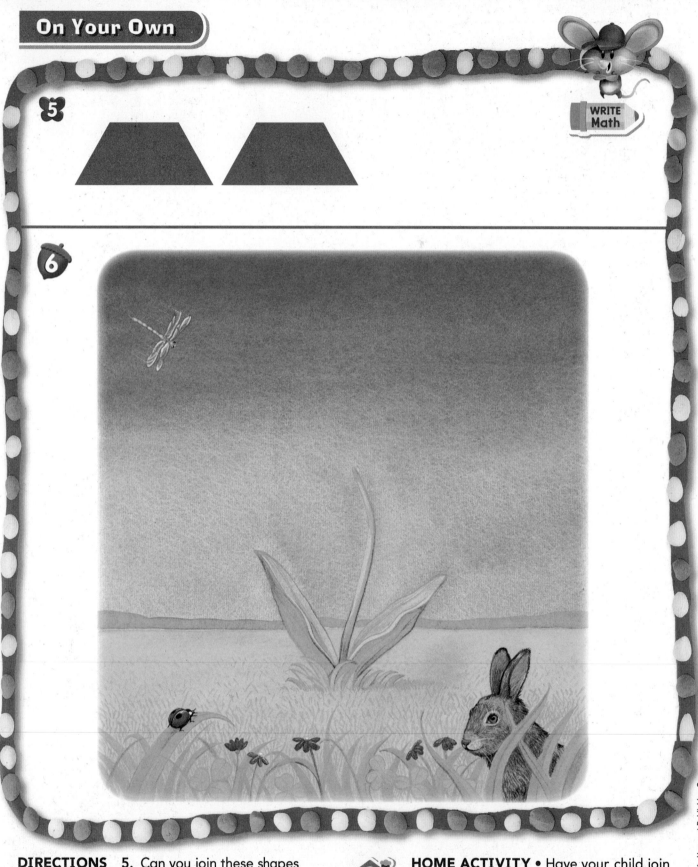

DIRECTIONS **5.** Can you join these shapes to make a hexagon? Use the shapes to draw a hexagon. **6.** Which shapes could you join to make a larger shape that looks like a flower? Draw and color to show the shapes you used.

HOME ACTIVITY • Have your child join shapes to form a larger shape, and then tell you about the shape.

562 five hundred sixty-two

Problem Solving • Draw to Join Shapes

Learning Objective You will use the strategy *draw a picture* by joining shapes to make new shapes to solve problems.

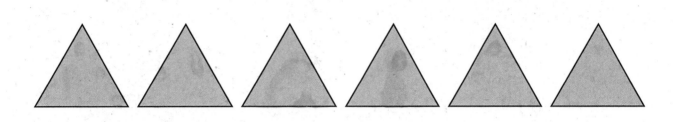

1

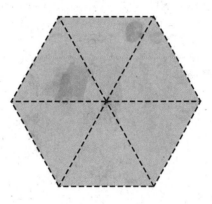

2

DIRECTIONS **1.** Place triangles on the page as shown. How can you join all of the triangles to make a hexagon? Trace around the triangles to draw the hexagon. **2.** How can you join some of the triangles to make a larger triangle? Trace around the triangles to draw the larger triangle.

Lesson Check

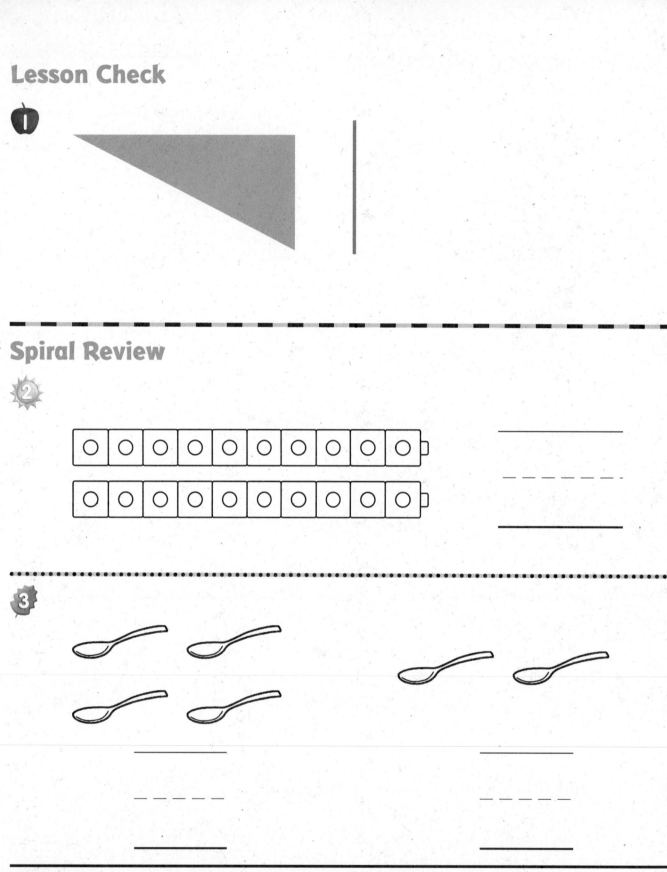

Spiral Review

DIRECTIONS
1. Join two triangles to make a shape. Draw and color the triangles you used. 2. Count and tell how many. Write the number. 3. Count and tell how many in each set. Write the numbers. Compare the numbers. Circle the number that is less.

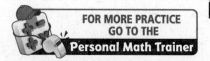

FOR MORE PRACTICE
GO TO THE
Personal Math Trainer

✓ Chapter 9 Review/Test

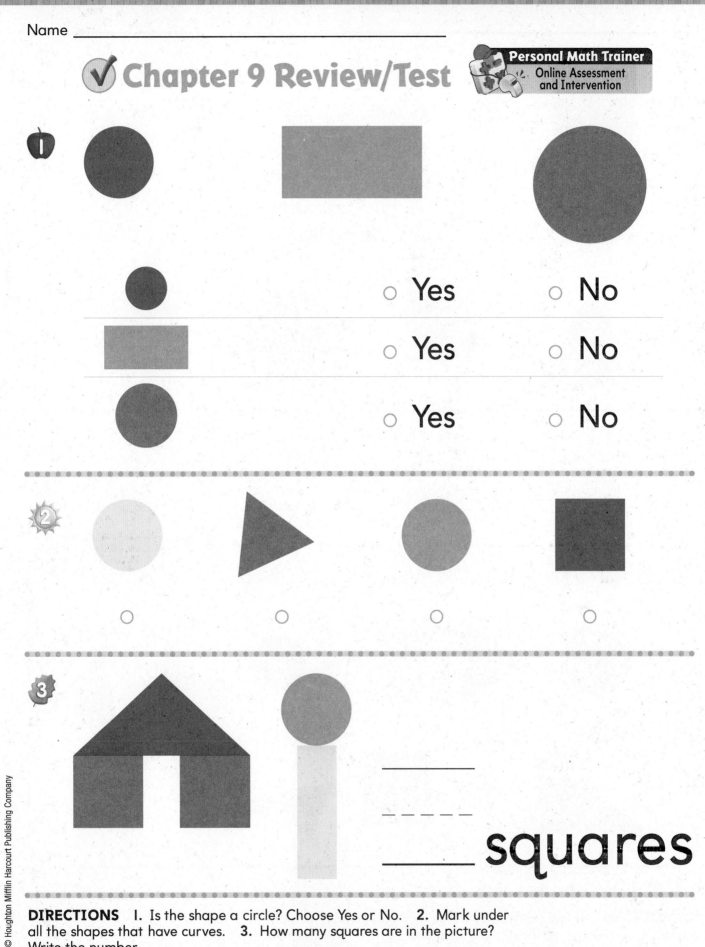

1.

○ Yes   ○ No

○ Yes   ○ No

○ Yes   ○ No

2.

○   ○   ○   ○

3.

_____
- - - - -
_____ squares

DIRECTIONS 1. Is the shape a circle? Choose Yes or No. 2. Mark under all the shapes that have curves. 3. How many squares are in the picture? Write the number.

 GO DIGITAL Assessment Options
Chapter Test

4

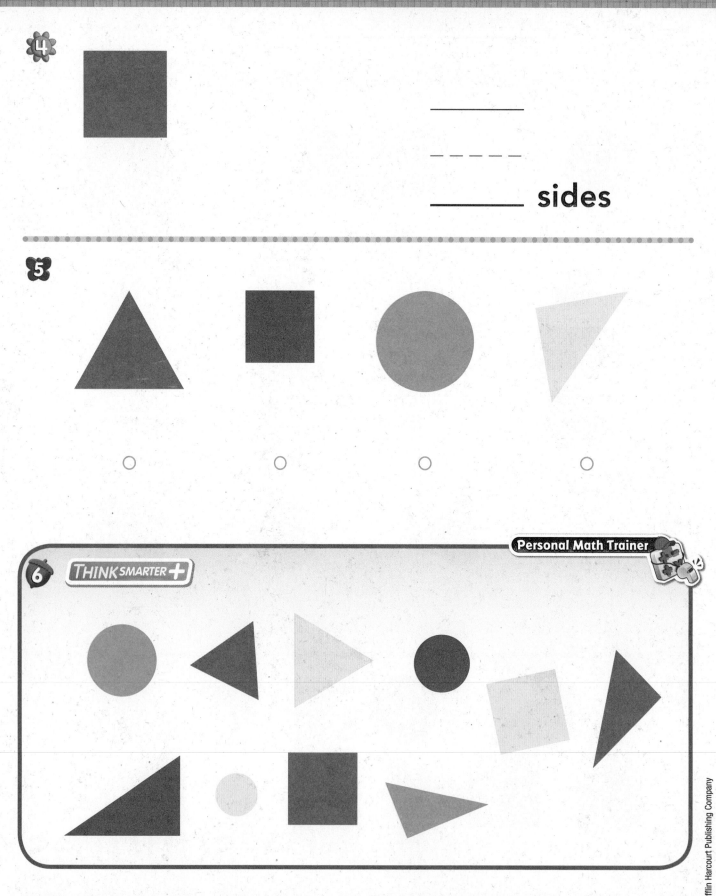

_____
- - - - -
_____ sides

5

○   ○   ○   ○

Personal Math Trainer

6 THINK SMARTER ✛

DIRECTIONS 4. Look at the square. Write the number of sides on a square. **5.** Mark under all of the shapes that are triangles. **6.** Mark an X on each shape that has 3 sides and 3 vertices.

566 five hundred sixty-six

© Houghton Mifflin Harcourt Publishing Company

Name _____

7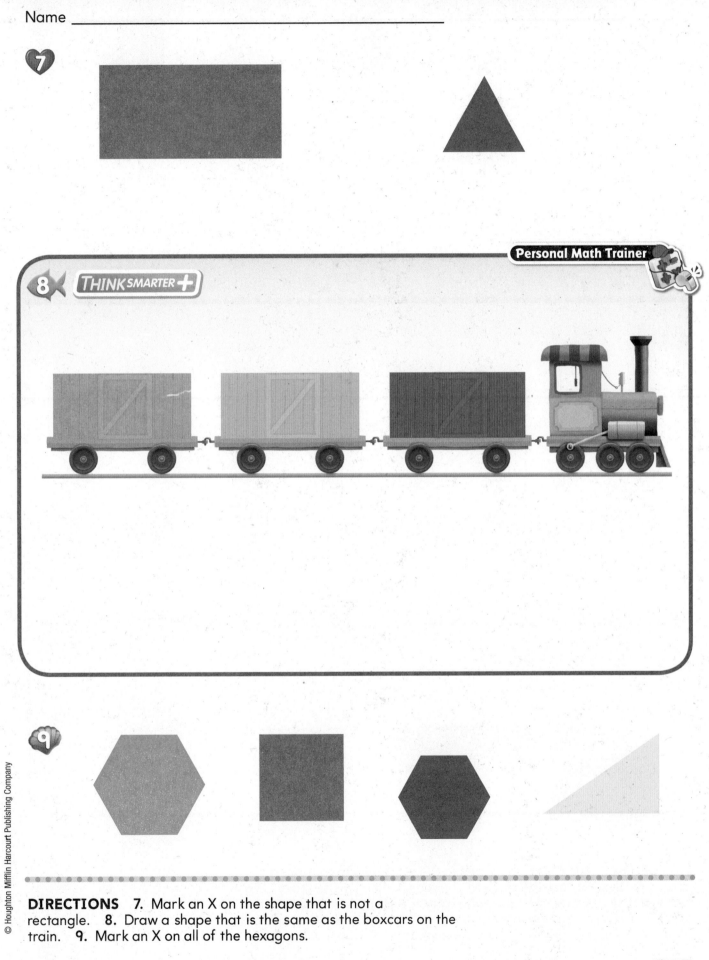

8 THINK SMARTER +

Personal Math Trainer

9

DIRECTIONS **7.** Mark an X on the shape that is not a rectangle. **8.** Draw a shape that is the same as the boxcars on the train. **9.** Mark an X on all of the hexagons.

Chapter 9

five hundred sixty-seven **567**

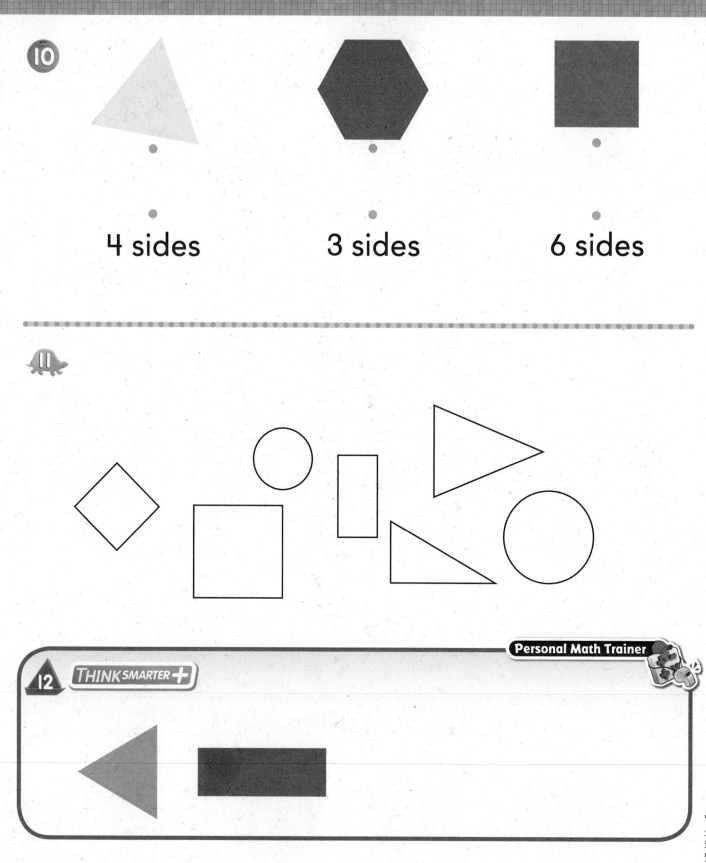

10

4 sides   3 sides   6 sides

11

12 THINK SMARTER +

Personal Math Trainer

DIRECTIONS 10. Match the shape to the number with that many sides. 11. Look at the shapes. Compare them to see how they are alike and how they are different. Use red to color the shapes with four sides. Use green to color the shapes with curves. Use blue to color the shapes with three vertices. 12. Join shapes to make an arrow. Draw the arrow.

Identify and Describe Three-Dimensional Shapes

Curious About Math with Curious George

Many of the shapes in our environment are three-dimensional shapes.

Name some of the shapes you see in this picture.

Name _____

Identify Shapes

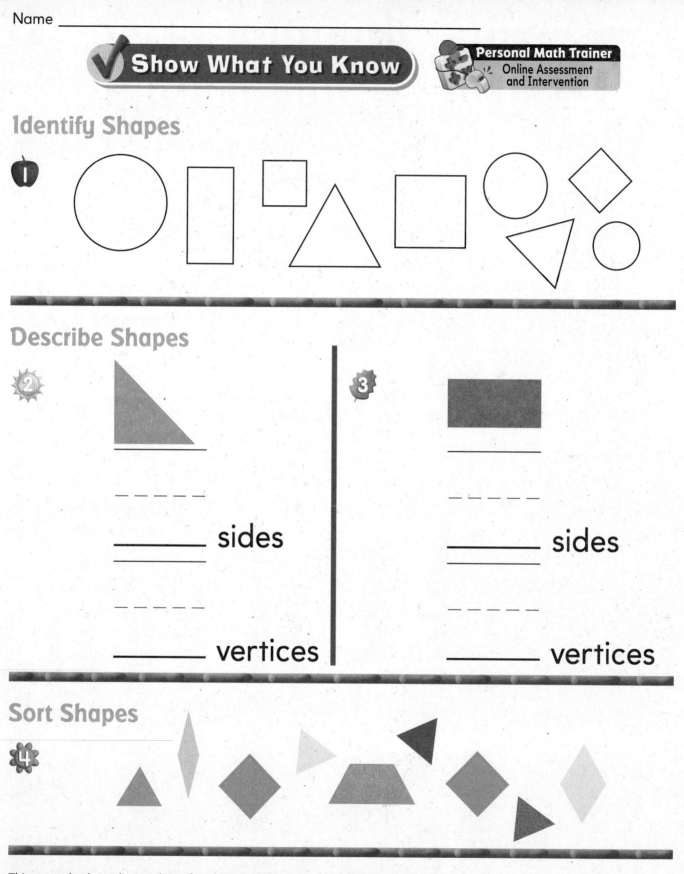

❶

Describe Shapes

❷

_____

- - - - - - - -

_____ sides

- - - - - - - -

_____ vertices

❸

_____

- - - - - - - -

_____ sides

- - - - - - - -

_____ vertices

Sort Shapes

❹

This page checks understanding of important skills needed for success in Chapter 10.

DIRECTIONS 1. Use red to color the squares. Use blue to color the triangles. 2–3. Look at the shape. Write how many sides. Write how many vertices. 4. Mark an X on the shapes with three sides.

Name _____

rectangle

circle

square

triangle

DIRECTIONS Mark an X on the food shaped like a circle. Draw a line under the food shaped like a square. Circle the food shaped like a triangle.

 • **Interactive Student Edition**
• **Multimedia *eGlossary***

Game Follow the Shapes

DIRECTIONS Choose a shape from START. Follow the path that has the same shapes. Draw a line to show the path to the END with the same shape.

Chapter 10 Vocabulary

above arriba, encima 1	**behind** detrás 5
below debajo 6	**beside** al lado 7
cone cono 14	**cube** cubo 15
curved surface superficie curva 17	**cylinder** cilindro 18

← **behind**

← **above**

The flowers are **beside** the tree.

below →

cube

cone

cylinder

curved surface

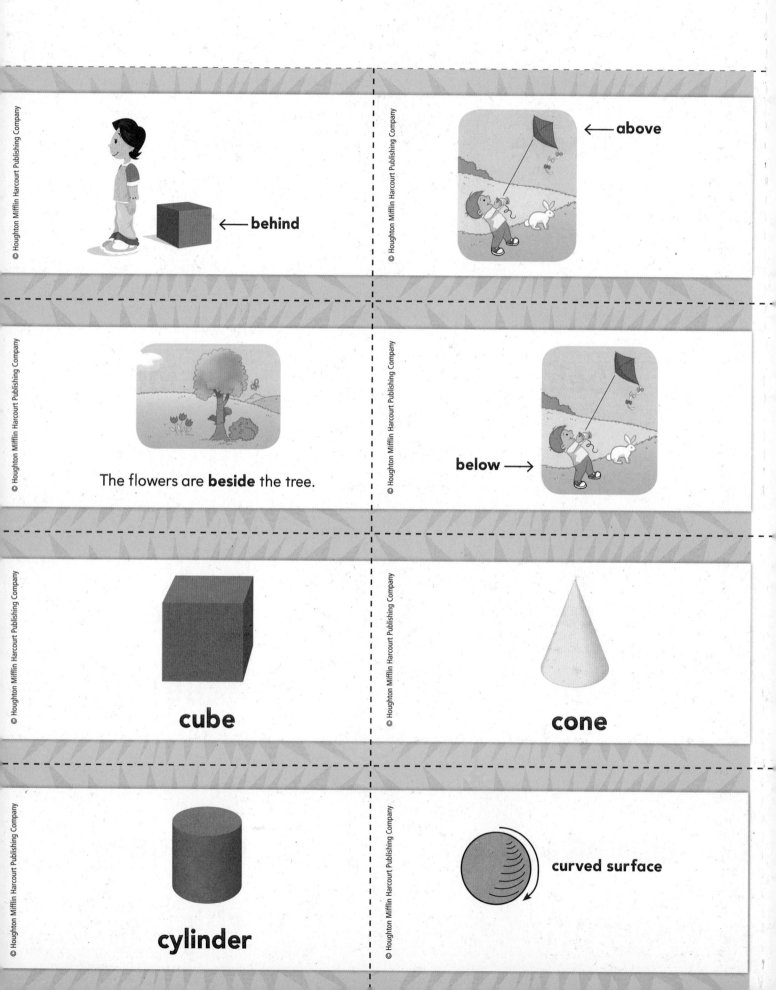

flat surface superficie plana 27	**in front of** delante de 35
next to al lado de 44	**roll** rodar 54
slide deslizar 67	**sphere** esfera 69
stack apilar 71	**three-dimensional shapes** figuras tridimensionales 78

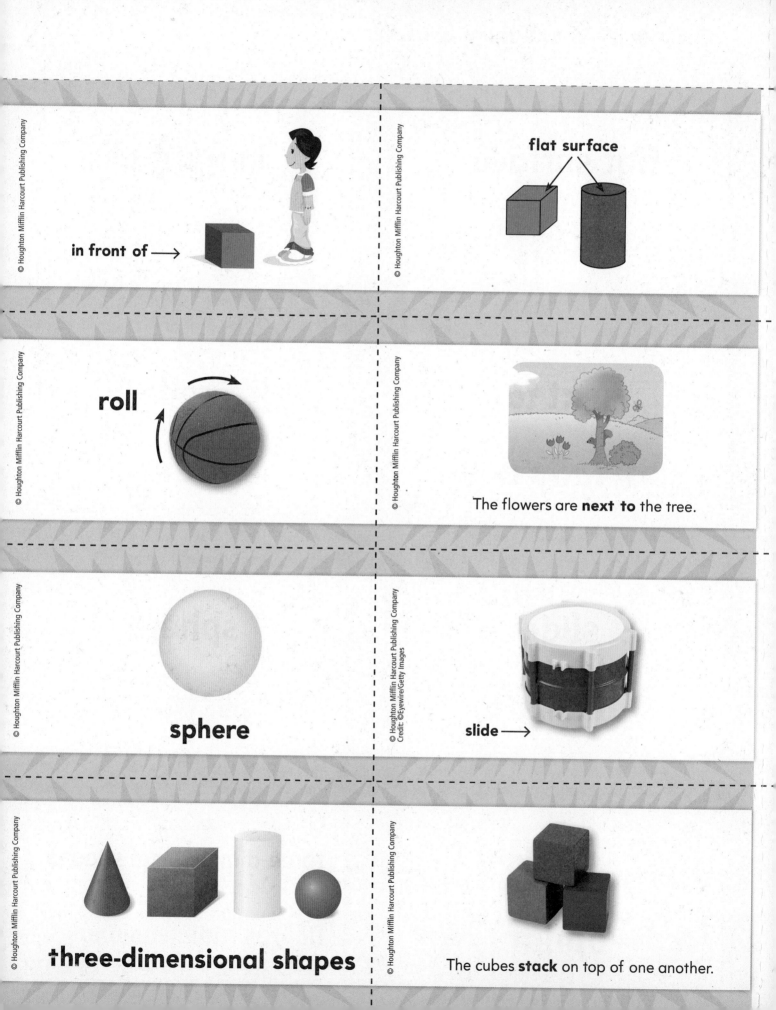

in front of →

flat surface

roll

The flowers are **next to** the tree.

sphere

slide →

three-dimensional shapes

The cubes **stack** on top of one another.

Picture It

Word Box
above
behind
below
beside
next to
in front of
cone
cube

Word Box
curved surface
cylinder
flat surface
roll
slide
sphere
stack
three-dimensional shape

Secret Words

Player 1

Player 2

DIRECTIONS Players take turns. A player chooses a secret word from the Word Box and then sets the timer. The player draws pictures to give hints about the secret word. If the other player guesses the secret word before time runs out, he or she puts a counter in the chart. The first player who has counters in all his or her boxes is the winner.

MATERIALS timer, drawing paper, two-color counters for each player

The Write Way

© Houghton Mifflin Harcourt Publishing Company • Image Credits: (bg) ©Studio-Pro/Getty Images; (r) ©Radoman Durkovic/Shutterstock

DIRECTIONS Choose one idea. • Choose 2 three-dimensional shapes. Draw to show what you know about the shapes. • Draw to show *above*, *below*, and *next to*.
Reflect Be ready to tell about your drawing.

Name _____

Three-Dimensional Shapes

Essential Question How can you show which shapes stack, roll, or slide?

Learning Objective You will show which shapes stack, roll, or slide and describe them using informal language.

does stack	does not stack

DIRECTIONS Place three-dimensional shapes on the page. Sort the shapes by whether they stack or do not stack. Describe the shapes. Match a picture of each shape to the shapes on the sorting mat. Glue the shape pictures on the sorting mat.

Chapter 10 • Lesson 1

five hundred seventy-three **573**

1 ☑

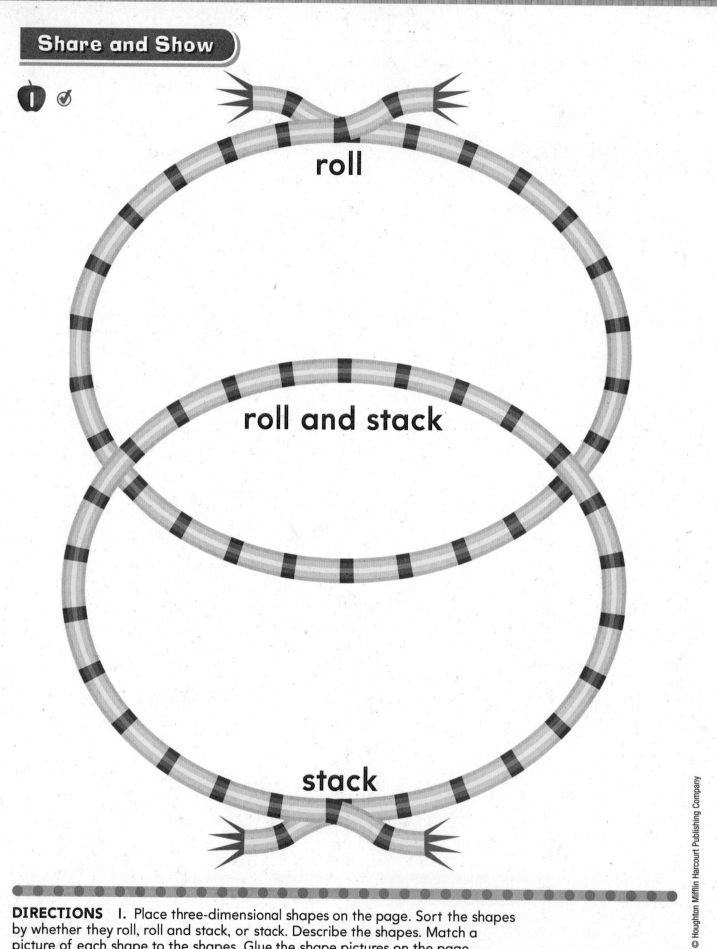

roll

roll and stack

stack

DIRECTIONS 1. Place three-dimensional shapes on the page. Sort the shapes by whether they roll, roll and stack, or stack. Describe the shapes. Match a picture of each shape to the shapes. Glue the shape pictures on the page.

Name _____

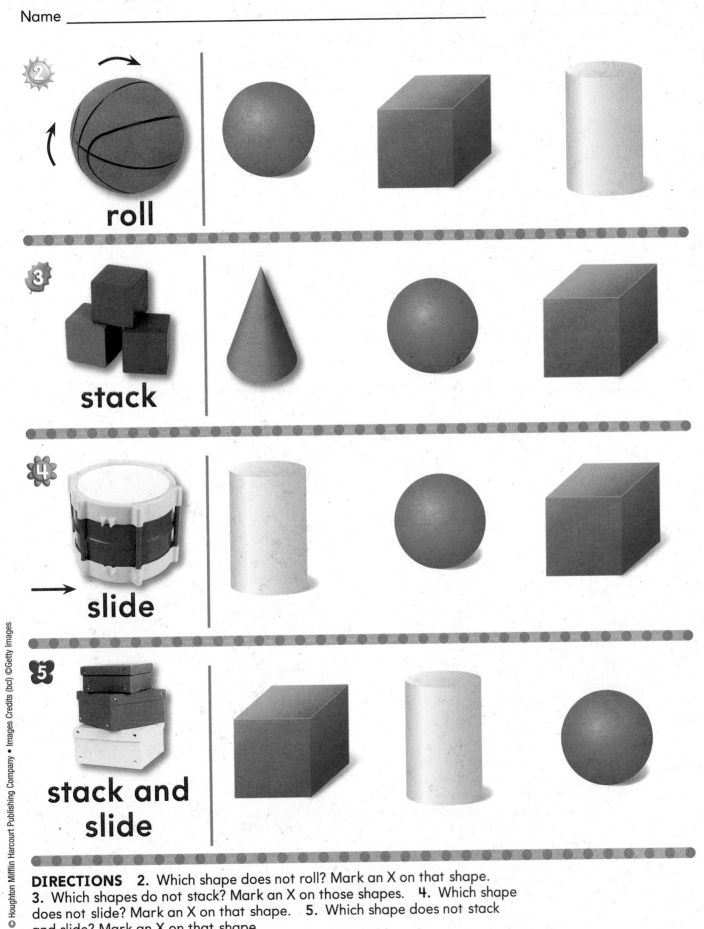

2 roll

3 stack

4 slide

5 stack and slide

DIRECTIONS 2. Which shape does not roll? Mark an X on that shape.
3. Which shapes do not stack? Mark an X on those shapes.   4. Which shape does not slide? Mark an X on that shape.   5. Which shape does not stack and slide? Mark an X on that shape.

Problem Solving • Applications

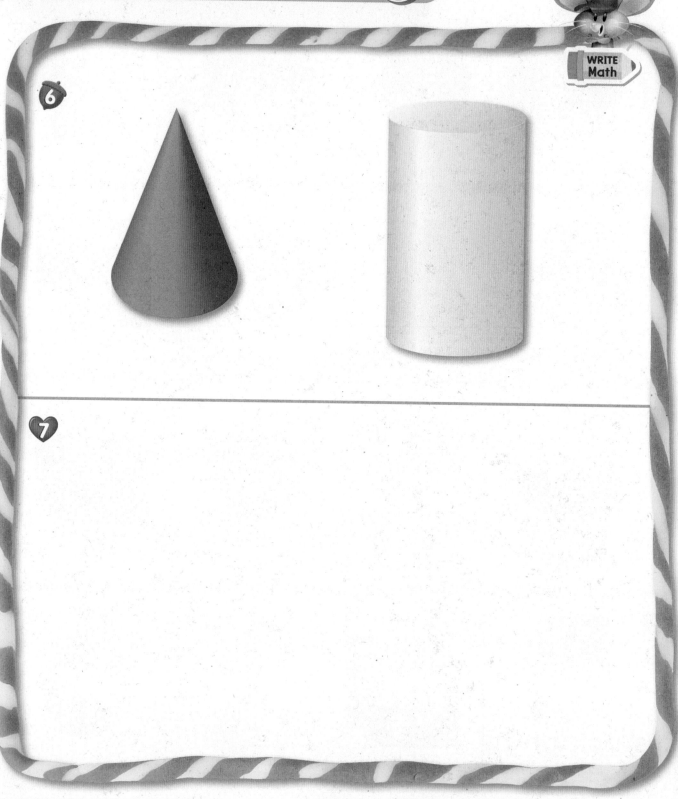

6.

7.

© Houghton Mifflin Harcourt Publishing Company

DIRECTIONS 6. I roll and do not stack. Describe the shape. Mark an X on that shape. **7.** Draw to show what you know about a real object that rolls and does not stack.

HOME ACTIVITY • Have your child identify and describe an object in the house that rolls and does not stack.

576 five hundred seventy-six

Three-Dimensional Shapes

Learning Objective You will show which shapes stack, roll, or slide and describe them using informal language.

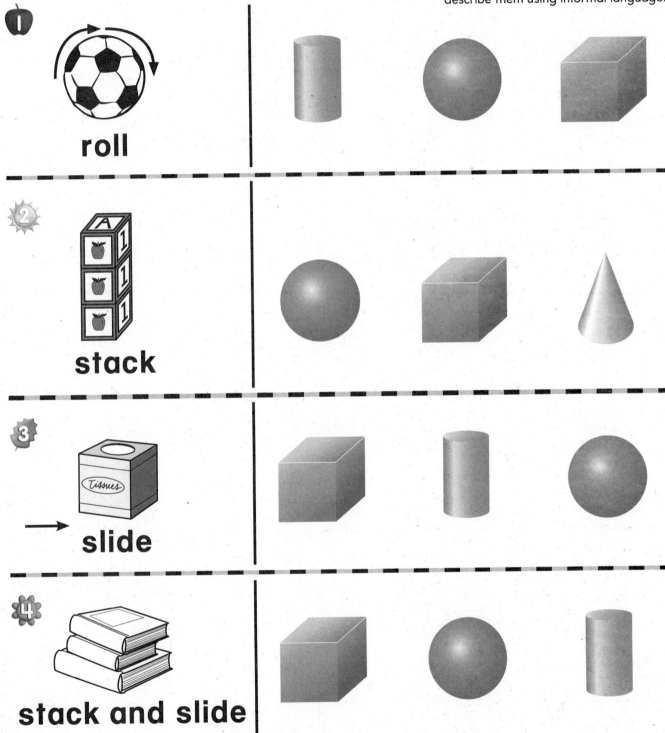

DIRECTIONS 1. Which shape does not roll? Mark an X on that shape. 2. Which shapes do not stack? Mark an X on those shapes. 3. Which shape does not slide? Mark an X on that shape. 4. Which shape does not stack and slide? Mark an X on that shape.

Chapter 10

five hundred seventy-seven **577**

Lesson Check

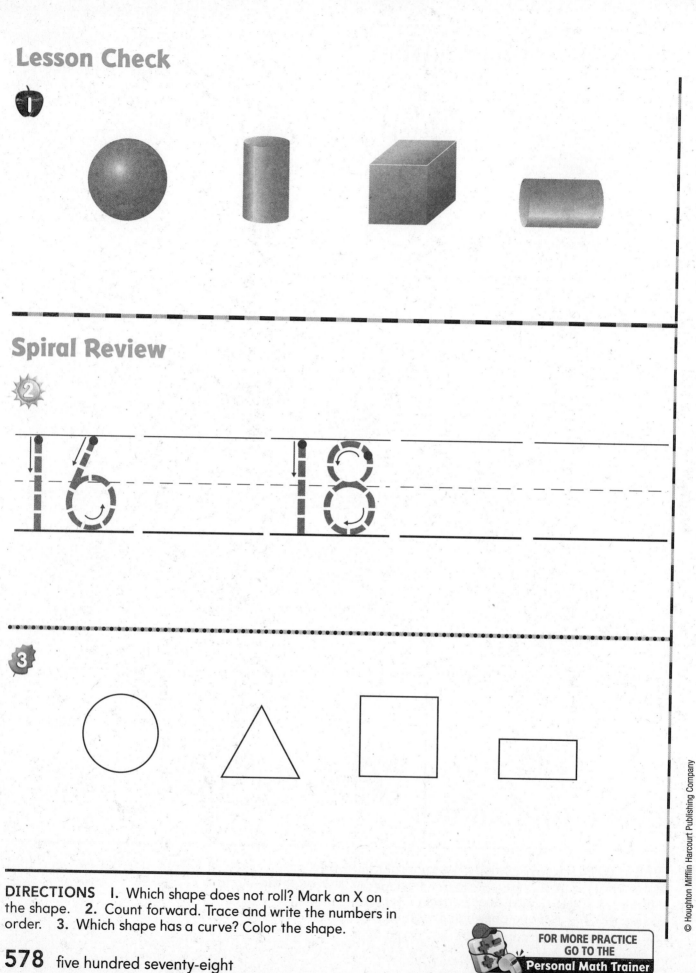

Spiral Review

DIRECTIONS 1. Which shape does not roll? Mark an X on the shape. 2. Count forward. Trace and write the numbers in order. 3. Which shape has a curve? Color the shape.

FOR MORE PRACTICE
GO TO THE
Personal Math Trainer

Name _____

Identify, Name, and Describe Spheres

Essential Question How can you identify, name, and describe spheres?

Learning Objective You will identify, name, and describe spheres using informal language.

Listen and Draw Real World Hands On

sphere	not a sphere

DIRECTIONS Place three-dimensional shapes on the page. Identify and name the sphere. Sort the shapes on the sorting mat. Describe the sphere. Match a picture of each shape to the shapes on the sorting mat. Glue the shape pictures on the sorting mat.

Chapter 10 • Lesson 2

1

sphere

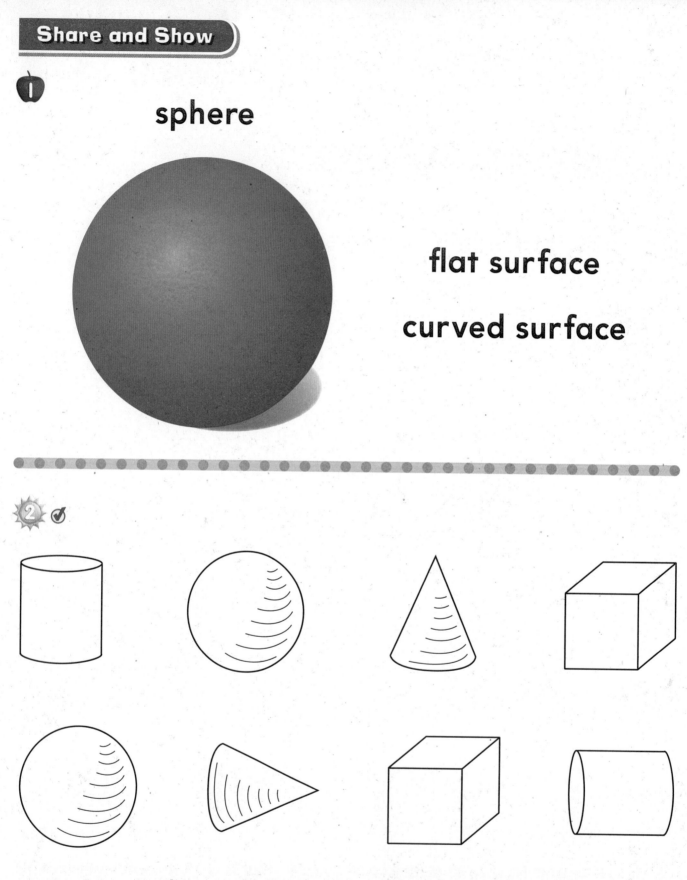

flat surface

curved surface

2 ✓

DIRECTIONS 1. Look at the sphere. Circle the words that describe a sphere. 2. Color the spheres.

Name _____

DIRECTIONS 3. Identify the objects that are shaped like a sphere. Mark an X on those objects.

Problem Solving • Applications Real World

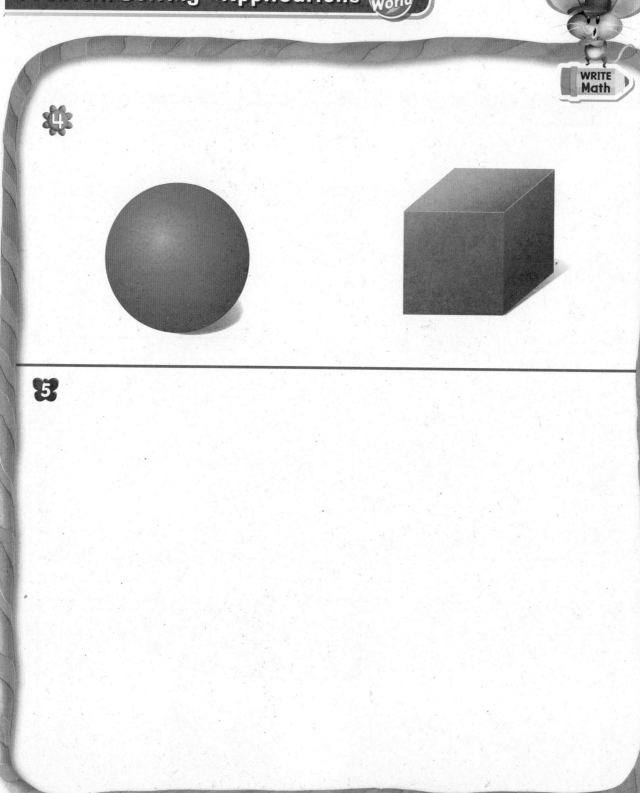

4

5

DIRECTIONS 4. I have a curved surface. Which shape am I? Mark an X on that shape. **5.** Draw to show what you know about a real object that is shaped like a sphere.

HOME ACTIVITY • Have your child identify and describe an object in the house that is shaped like a sphere.

Name _____

Identify, Name, and Describe Spheres

Learning Objective You will identify, name, and describe spheres using informal language.

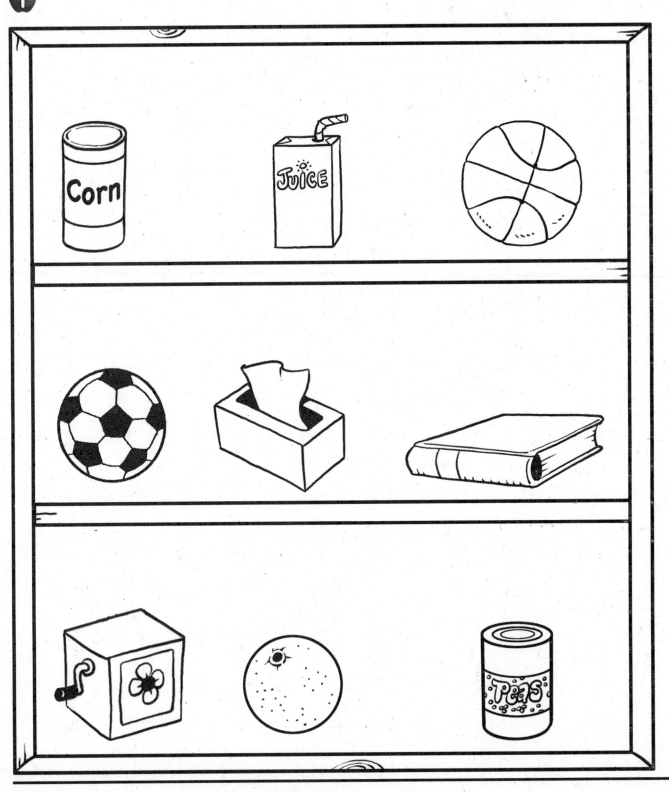

DIRECTIONS 1. Identify the objects that are shaped like a sphere. Mark an X on those objects.

Chapter 10

Lesson Check

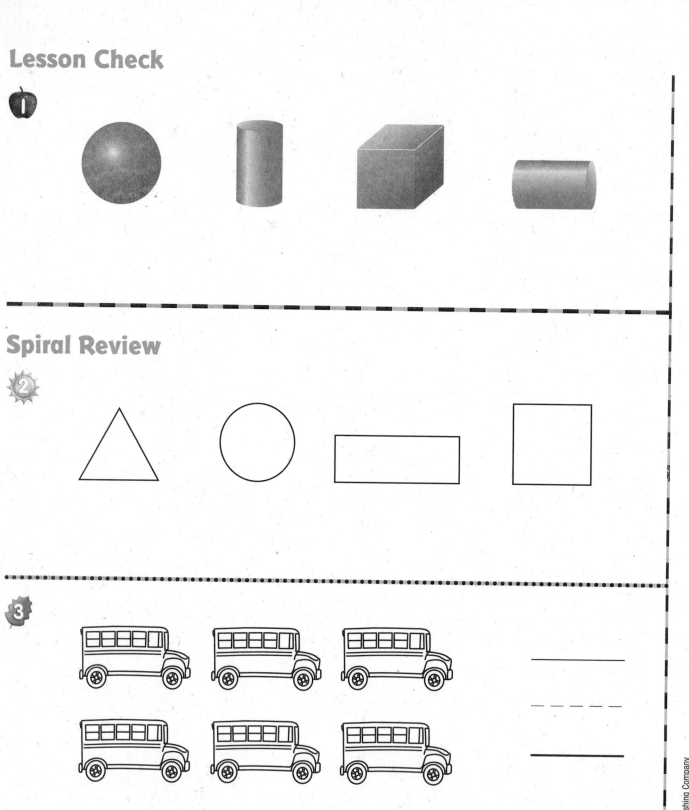

Spiral Review

DIRECTIONS **1.** Which shape is a sphere? Mark an X on the shape. **2.** Which shape is a square? Color the square. **3.** How many school buses are there? Write the number.

FOR MORE PRACTICE
GO TO THE
Personal Math Trainer

Name _____

Identify, Name, and Describe Cubes

Essential Question How can you identify, name, and describe cubes?

Learning Objective You will identify, name, and describe cubes using informal language.

Listen and Draw Real World Hands On

cube	not a cube

DIRECTIONS Place three-dimensional shapes on the page. Identify and name the cube. Sort the shapes on the sorting mat. Describe the cube. Match a picture of each shape to the shapes on the sorting mat. Glue the shape pictures on the sorting mat.

Chapter 10 • Lesson 3

cube

flat surface

curved surface

_____

_ _ _ _ _

_____ flat surfaces

DIRECTIONS 1. Look at the cube. Circle the words that describe a cube. 2. Use a cube to count how many flat surfaces. Write the number.

Name _____

DIRECTIONS **3.** Identify the objects that are shaped like a cube. Mark an X on those objects.

Chapter 10 • Lesson 3   five hundred eighty-seven **587**

Problem Solving • Applications   Real World

WRITE
Math

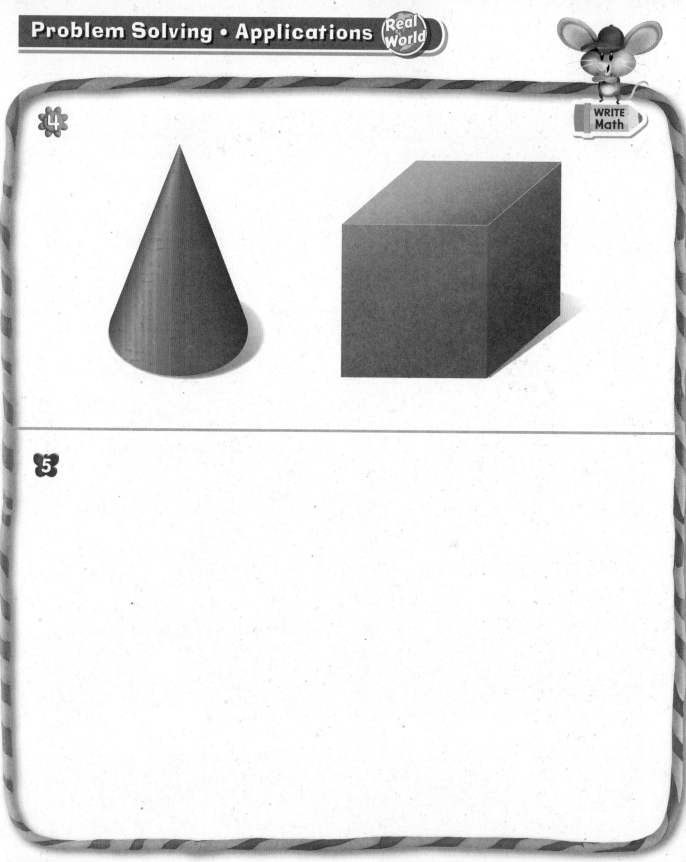

4

5

DIRECTIONS **4.** I have 6 flat surfaces. Which shape am I? Mark an X on that shape. **5.** Draw to show what you know about a real object that is shaped like a cube.

HOME ACTIVITY • Have your child identify and describe an object in the house that is shaped like a cube.

Identify, Name, and Describe Cubes

Learning Objective You will identify, name, and describe cubes using informal language.

DIRECTIONS I. Identify the objects that are shaped like a cube. Mark an X on those objects.

Lesson Check

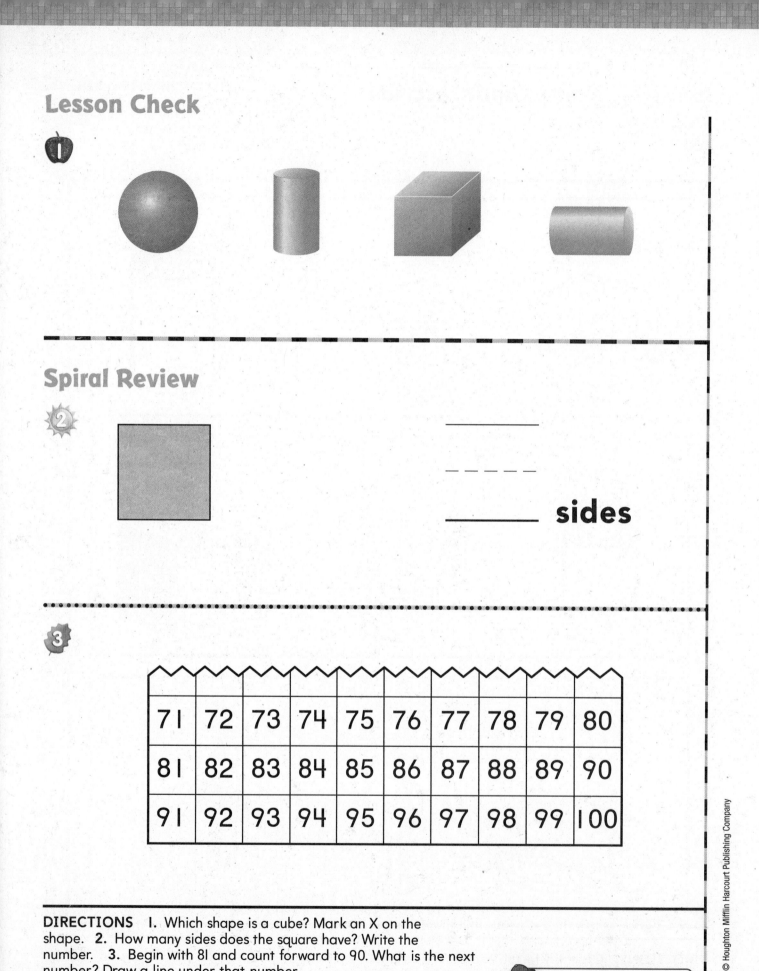

1

Spiral Review

2

_____

- - - - - - -

_____ **sides**

3

71	72	73	74	75	76	77	78	79	80
81	82	83	84	85	86	87	88	89	90
91	92	93	94	95	96	97	98	99	100

DIRECTIONS **1.** Which shape is a cube? Mark an X on the shape. **2.** How many sides does the square have? Write the number. **3.** Begin with 81 and count forward to 90. What is the next number? Draw a line under that number.

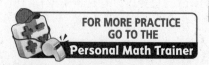

FOR MORE PRACTICE
GO TO THE
Personal Math Trainer

Name _____

Identify, Name, and Describe Cylinders

Essential Question How can you identify, name, and describe cylinders?

Learning Objective You will identify, name, and describe cylinders using informal language.

Listen and Draw Real World

cylinder	not a cylinder

DIRECTIONS Place three-dimensional shapes on the page. Identify and name the cylinder. Sort the shapes on the sorting mat. Describe the cylinder. Match a picture of each shape to the shapes on the sorting mat. Glue the shape pictures on the sorting mat.

© Houghton Mifflin Harcourt Publishing Company

Chapter 10 • Lesson 4

1

cylinder

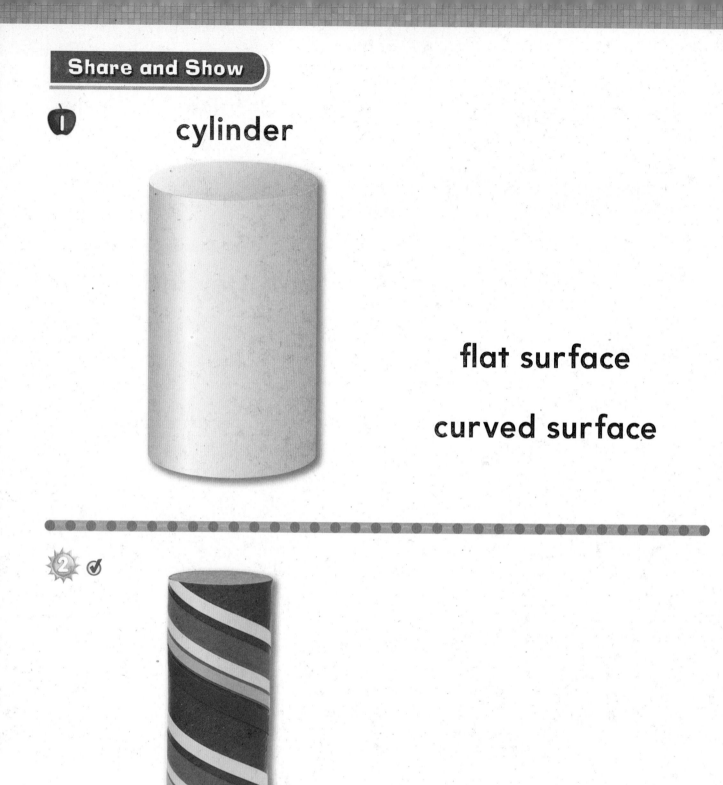

flat surface

curved surface

2 ✓

_____

- - - - -

_____ flat surfaces

DIRECTIONS 1. Look at the cylinder. Circle the words that describe a cylinder.
2. Use a cylinder to count how many flat surfaces. Write the number.

Name _____

③

DIRECTIONS 3. Identify the objects that are shaped like a cylinder. Mark an X on those objects.

Chapter 10 • Lesson 4

Problem Solving • Applications

4

5

© Houghton Mifflin Harcourt Publishing Company

DIRECTIONS 4. I have 2 flat surfaces. Which shape am I? Mark an X on that shape. 5. Draw to show what you know about a real object that is shaped like a cylinder.

HOME ACTIVITY • Have your child identify and describe an object in the house that is shaped like a cylinder.

Name _____

Identify, Name, and Describe Cylinders

Learning Objective You will identify, name, and describe cylinders using informal language.

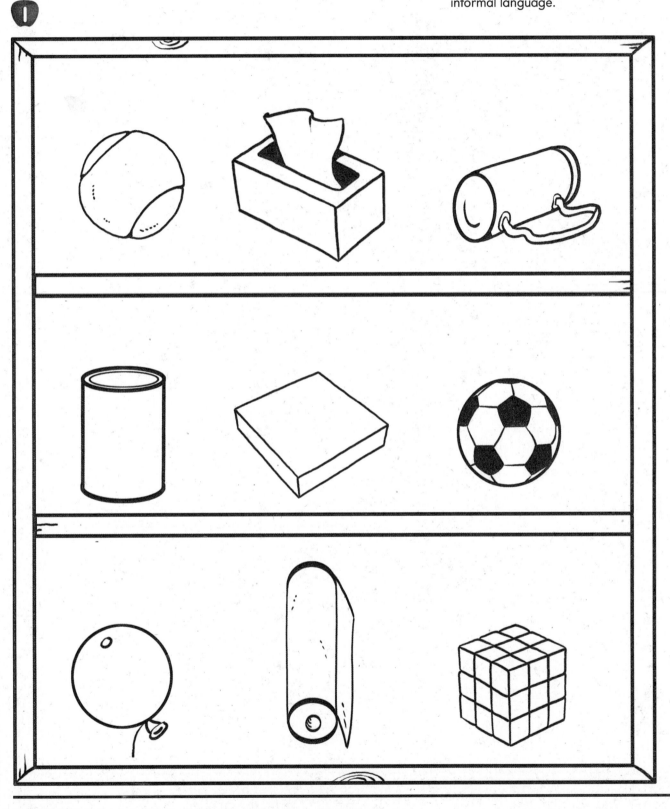

DIRECTIONS I. Identify the objects that are shaped like a cylinder. Mark an X on those objects.

Chapter 10

five hundred ninety-five **595**

Lesson Check

1

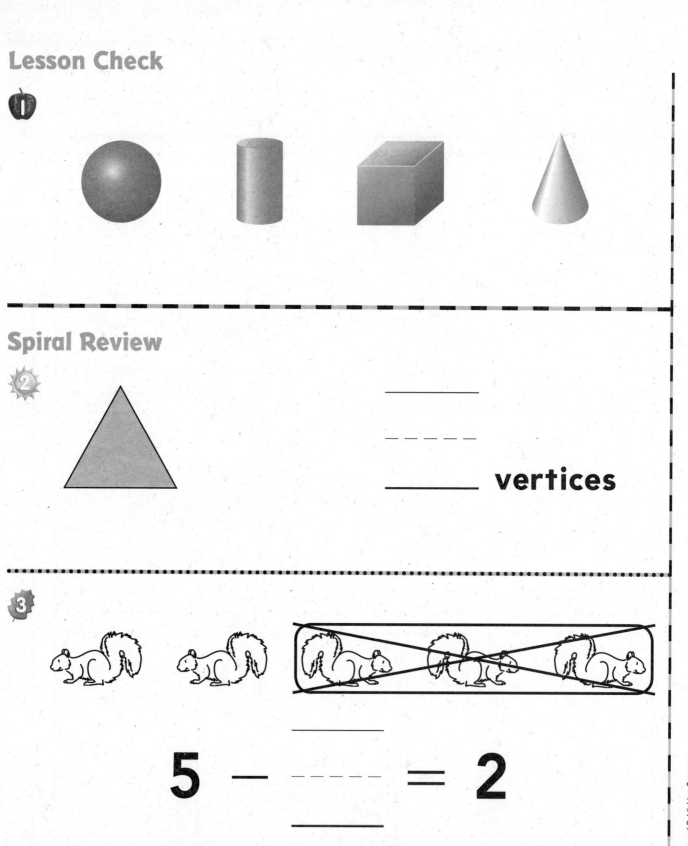

Spiral Review

2

_____

- - - - - - - -

_____ **vertices**

3

5   −   _____   =   2

DIRECTIONS 1. Which shape is a cylinder? Mark an X on the shape. 2. How many vertices does the triangle have? Write the number. 3. Write the number to show how many are being taken from the set.

596 five hundred ninety-six

FOR MORE PRACTICE
GO TO THE
Personal Math Trainer

Identify, Name, and Describe Cones

Essential Question How can you identify, name, and describe cones?

Learning Objective You will identify, name, and describe cones using informal language.

Listen and Draw Real World

cone	not a cone

DIRECTIONS Place three-dimensional shapes on the page. Identify and name the cone. Sort the shapes on the sorting mat. Describe the cone. Match a picture of each shape to the shapes on the sorting mat. Glue the shape pictures on the sorting mat.

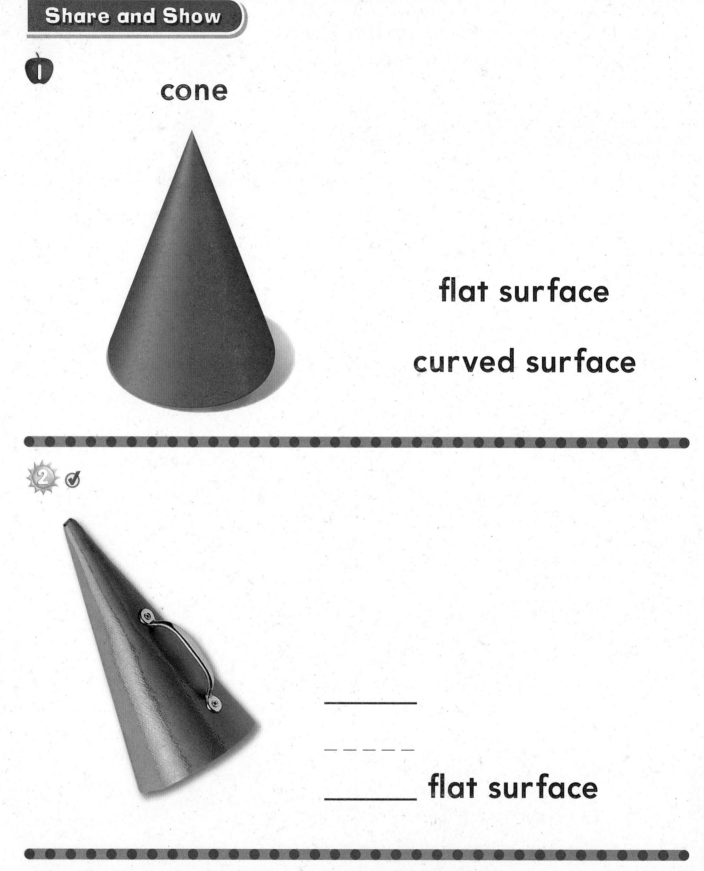

1

cone

flat surface

curved surface

2 ✓

_____

- - - - -

_____ flat surface

DIRECTIONS 1. Look at the cone. Circle the words that describe a cone. 2. Use a cone to count how many flat surfaces. Write the number.

Name _____

DIRECTIONS 3. Identify the objects that are shaped like a cone. Mark an X on those objects.

HOME ACTIVITY • Have your child identify and describe an object in the house that is shaped like a cone.

Chapter 10 • Lesson 5

five hundred ninety-nine **599**

Concepts and Skills

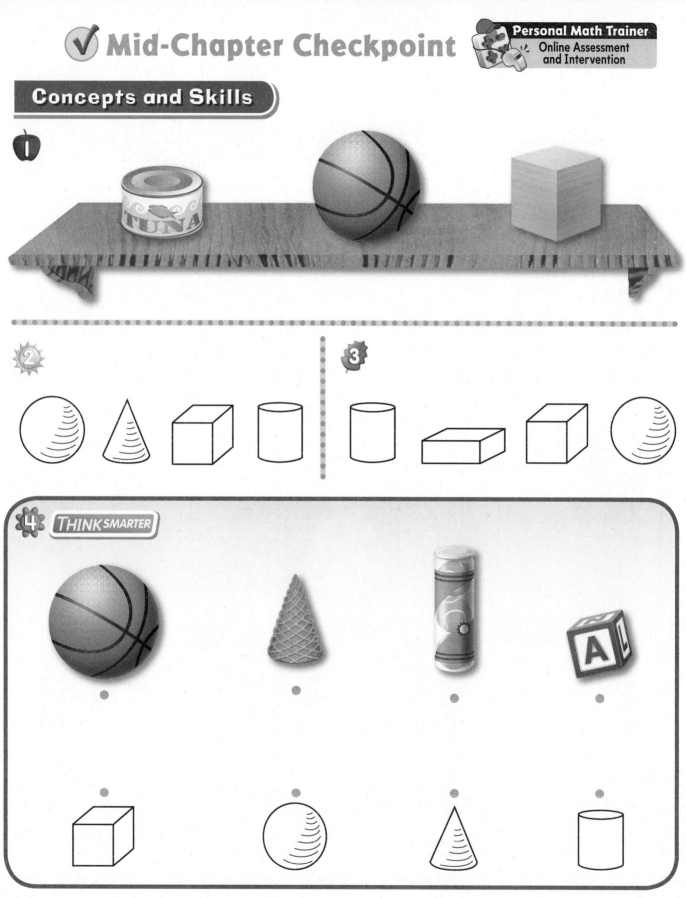

DIRECTIONS 1. Mark an X on the object that is shaped like a cylinder.
2. Color the sphere. 3. Color the cube. 4. Draw lines to match the objects to their shapes.

Identify, Name, and Describe Cones

Learning Objective You will identify, name, and describe cones using informal language.

DIRECTIONS 1. Identify the objects that are shaped like a cone. Mark an X on those objects.

Chapter 10

Lesson Check

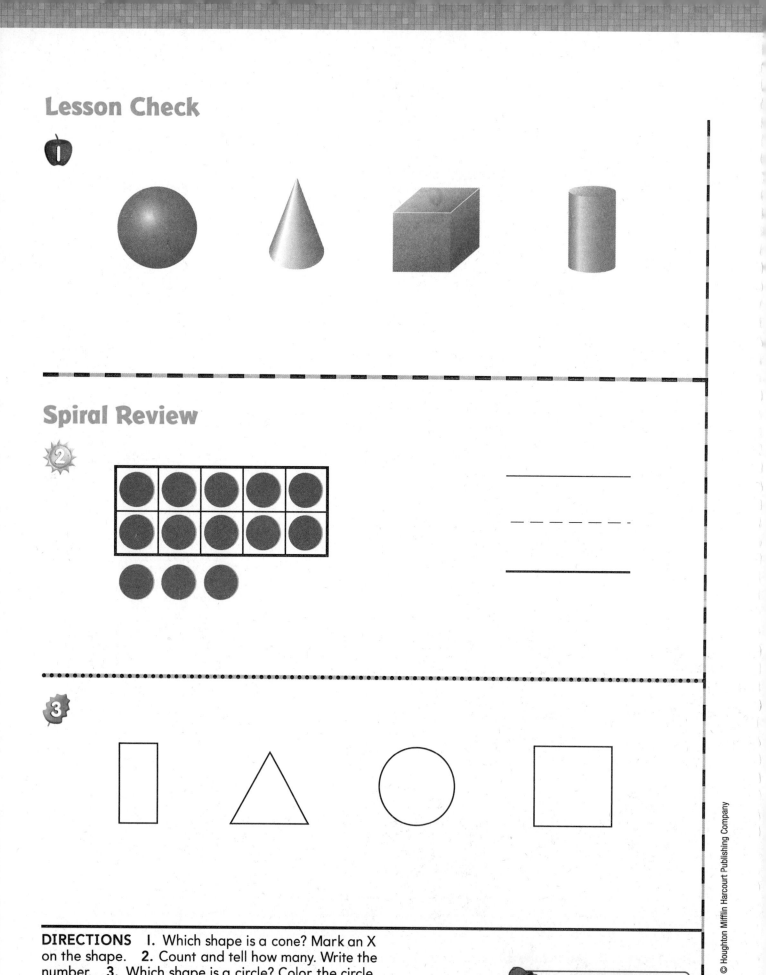

Spiral Review

DIRECTIONS 1. Which shape is a cone? Mark an X on the shape. 2. Count and tell how many. Write the number. 3. Which shape is a circle? Color the circle.

FOR MORE PRACTICE GO TO THE Personal Math Trainer

Name _____

Problem Solving • Two- and Three-Dimensional Shapes

Essential Question How can you solve problems using the strategy **use logical reasoning**?

Learning Objective You will use the strategy *use logical reasoning* by sorting two- and three-dimensional shapes to solve problems.

🔑 Unlock the Problem Real World

two-dimensional shapes	three-dimensional shapes

DIRECTIONS Place shapes on the page. Sort the shapes on the sorting mat into sets of two-dimensional and three-dimensional shapes. Match a picture of each shape to a shape on the sorting mat. Glue the shape pictures on the sorting mat.

Chapter 10 • Lesson 6

six hundred three **603**

Try Another Problem

DIRECTIONS 1. Identify the two-dimensional or flat shapes. Trace the circle around the square. Circle the other flat shapes. Identify the three-dimensional or solid shapes. Trace the X on the sphere. Mark an X on the other solid shapes.

Name _____

DIRECTIONS 2. Identify the two-dimensional or flat shapes.
Use red to color the flat shapes. Identify the three-dimensional
or solid shapes. Use blue to color the solid shapes.

Chapter 10 • Lesson 6

six hundred five **605**

On Your Own Real World

WRITE Math

3

4

© Houghton Mifflin Harcourt Publishing Company

DIRECTIONS 3. Draw to show what you know about a flat shape. Name the shape. 4. Draw to show what you know about a real object that has a solid shape. Name the object and the shape.

HOME ACTIVITY • Have your child identify a household object that is shaped like a three-dimensional shape. Have him or her name the three-dimensional shape.

Problem Solving • Two- and Three-Dimensional Shapes

Learning Objective You will use the strategy *use logical reasoning* by sorting two- and three-dimensional shapes to solve problems.

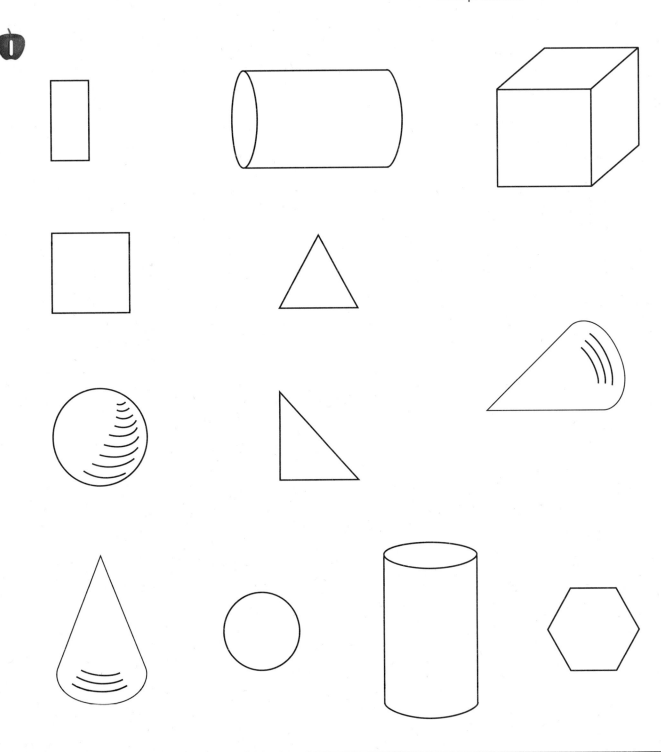

DIRECTIONS 1. Identify the two-dimensional or flat shapes. Use red to color the flat shapes. Identify the three-dimensional or solid shapes. Use blue to color the solid shapes.

Lesson Check

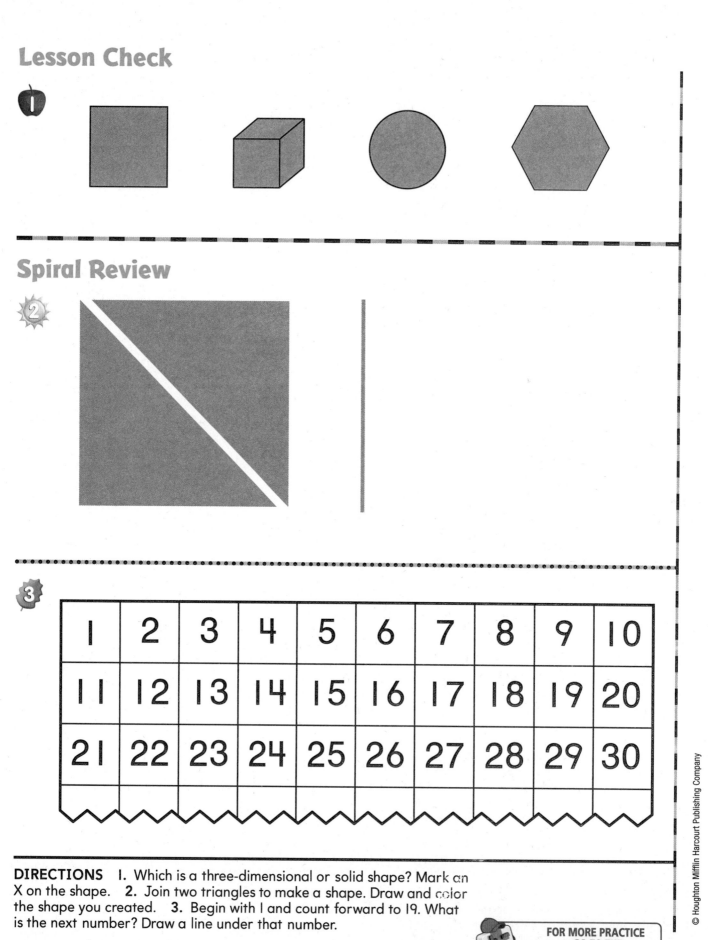

Spiral Review

1	2	3	4	5	6	7	8	9	10
11	12	13	14	15	16	17	18	19	20
21	22	23	24	25	26	27	28	29	30

DIRECTIONS **1.** Which is a three-dimensional or solid shape? Mark an X on the shape. **2.** Join two triangles to make a shape. Draw and color the shape you created. **3.** Begin with 1 and count forward to 19. What is the next number? Draw a line under that number.

608 six hundred eight

© Houghton Mifflin Harcourt Publishing Company

FOR MORE PRACTICE
GO TO THE
Personal Math Trainer

Name _____

Model Shapes

Essential Question How can you model shapes in the real world?

Learning Objective You will model shapes in the world by composing flat and solid shapes using straws and clay.

DIRECTIONS Use your finger to trace around the shape. Name the shape. Tell a friend whether this shape is flat or solid. Talk about the number of sides and the number of vertices.

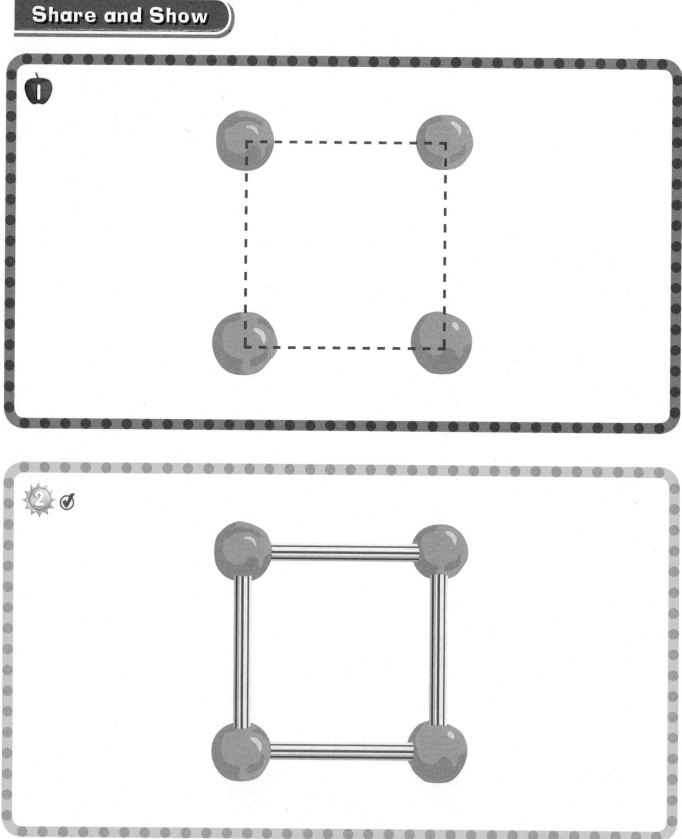

DIRECTIONS 1. Use clay to model 4 spheres as shown. Trace the square. The clay spheres will model the corners of the squares. 2. Place straws into the spheres as shown.

Name _____

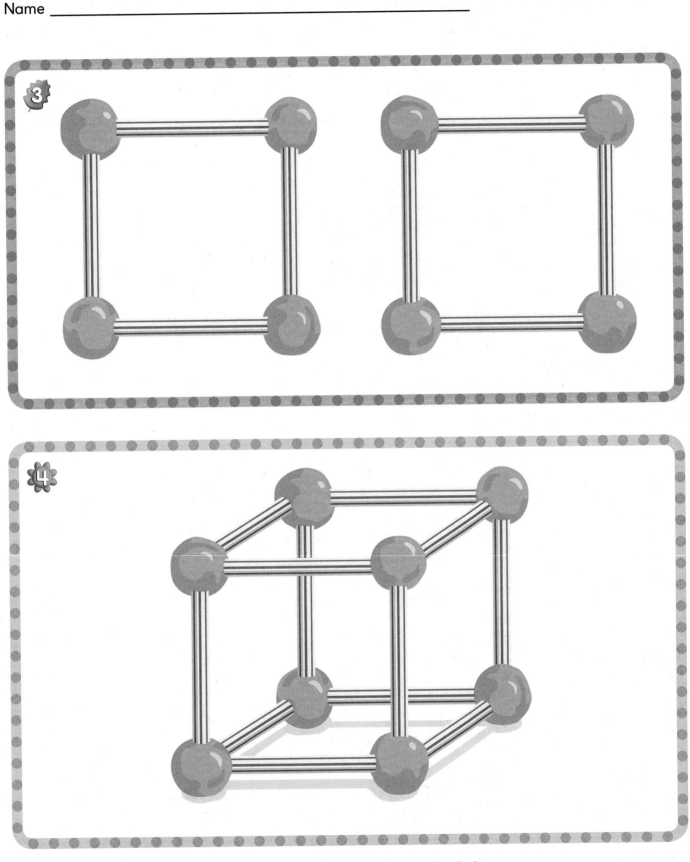

DIRECTIONS **3.** Use clay and straws to model another shape. Match the shape that you modeled in Exercise 2. **4.** Stand a straw into each corner of one of the shapes. Carefully lift the other shape and place it onto the straws as shown. Name the solid shape you modeled.

© Houghton Mifflin Harcourt Publishing Company

Chapter 10 • Lesson 7

six hundred eleven **611**

Problem Solving • Applications

5

6

DIRECTIONS 5. Maria's window has the shape of a square. Draw a picture of the shape. Tell a friend whether this shape is flat or solid. Talk about the number of sides and the number of vertices. 6. Use objects such as clay and straws to model a solid shape. Draw a picture of the solid shape. Tell a friend about the shape.

HOME ACTIVITY • Have your child identify a household object that has a flat shape. Have your child model the shape with a drawing. Repeat the activity with a solid object, and have your child model the shape with materials such as clay and toothpicks.

Model Shapes

Learning Objective You will model shapes in the world by composing flat and solid shapes using straws and clay.

①

_____

- - - - -

_____ **sides**

②

_____

- - - - -

_____ **flat surfaces**

DIRECTIONS 1. Draw to show what you know about a square. Write how many sides. 2. Declan's can of corn has the shape of a cylinder. Use clay to model a cylinder. Draw the cylinder. How many flat surfaces are there? Write the number.

Chapter 10

Lesson Check

1

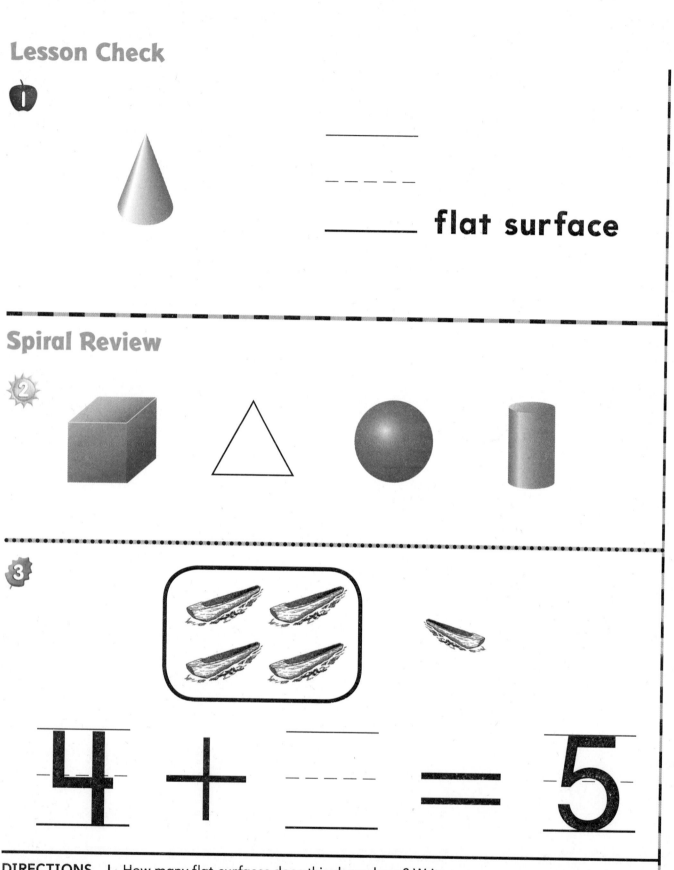

_____

- - - - - - -

_____ **flat surface**

Spiral Review

2

3

$$4 + \underline{\quad} = 5$$

DIRECTIONS 1. How many flat surfaces does this shape have? Write the number. 2. Which shape is flat? Color the flat shape. 3. Tell an addition word problem about the boats. Write the number to complete the addition sentence.

614 six hundred fourteen

Name _____

Above and Below

Essential Question How can you use the terms *above* and *below* to describe shapes in the environment?

Learning Objective You will use the terms *above* and *below* to describe the positions of objects in space.

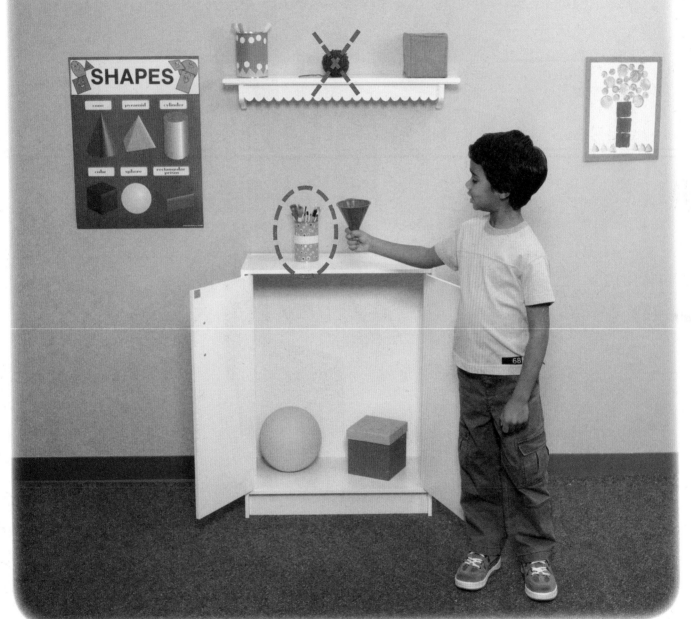

DIRECTIONS Trace the circle around the object shaped like a cylinder that is below the shelf. Trace the X on the object shaped like a sphere that is above the cabinet.

© Houghton Mifflin Harcourt Publishing Company

Chapter 10 • Lesson 8

six hundred fifteen **615**

1

DIRECTIONS **I.** Circle the object that is shaped like a cone below the play set. Mark an X on the object that is shaped like a cube above the play set. Color the object that is shaped like a cylinder above the play set.

Name _____

DIRECTIONS   2. Circle the object shaped like a sphere above the net. Mark an X on the object shaped like a cube directly below the net.

Chapter 10 • Lesson 8

six hundred seventeen **617**

Problem Solving • Applications (Real World)

③

WRITE Math

DIRECTIONS 3. Draw to show what you know about real world three-dimensional objects that might be above or below the net. Tell a friend about your drawing as you name the shape of the objects.

HOME ACTIVITY • Tell your child you are thinking of something in the room that is above or below another object. Have your child tell you what the object might be.

Name _____

Above and Below

Learning Objective You will use the terms *above* and *below* to describe the positions of objects in space.

DIRECTIONS **1.** Mark an X on the object that is shaped like a sphere below the table. Circle the object that is shaped like a cube above the table.

Chapter 10

six hundred nineteen **619**

Lesson Check

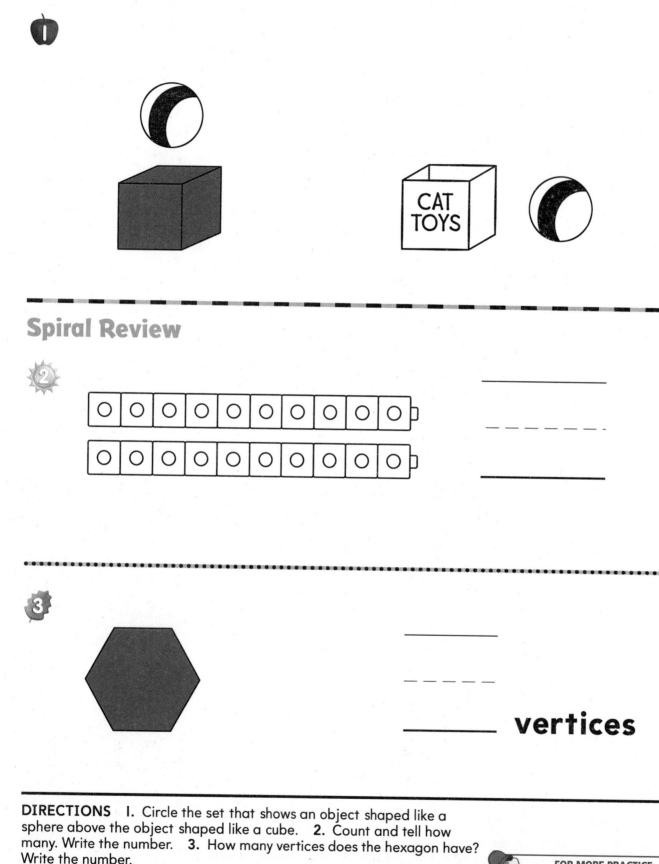

Spiral Review

_____

_ _ _ _ _ _ _ _

_____

_____

_ _ _ _ _ _ _ _

_____ **vertices**

DIRECTIONS **1.** Circle the set that shows an object shaped like a sphere above the object shaped like a cube. **2.** Count and tell how many. Write the number. **3.** How many vertices does the hexagon have? Write the number.

620 six hundred twenty

**FOR MORE PRACTICE
GO TO THE
Personal Math Trainer**

Name _____

Beside and Next To

Essential Question How can you use the terms *beside* and *next to* to describe shapes in the environment?

Learning Objective You will use the terms *beside* and *next to* to describe the positions of objects in space.

DIRECTIONS Trace the X on the object shaped like a cone that is beside the object shaped like a sphere. Trace the circle around the object shaped like a sphere that is next to the object shaped like a cube.

Share and Show

1

DIRECTIONS 1. Mark an X on the bead shaped like a cube that is beside the bead shaped like a cone. Draw a circle around the bead shaped like a cone that is next to the bead shaped like a cylinder. Use the words *next to* and *beside* to name the position of other bead shapes.

622 six hundred twenty-two

Name _____

DIRECTIONS 2. Mark an X on the object shaped like a cylinder that is next to the object shaped like a sphere. Draw a circle around the object shaped like a cone that is beside the object shaped like a cube. Use the words *next to* and *beside* to describe the position of other package shapes.

Problem Solving • Applications

3

WRITE Math

DIRECTIONS **3.** Draw or use pictures to show what you know about real world three-dimensional objects beside and next to other objects.

HOME ACTIVITY • Tell your child you are thinking of something in the room that is beside or next to another object. Have your child tell you the shape of the object.

624 six hundred twenty-four

Name _____

Beside and Next To

Learning Objective You will use the terms *beside* and *next to* to describe the positions of objects in space.

DIRECTIONS **1.** Mark an X on the object shaped like a cylinder that is next to the object shaped like a sphere. Circle the object shaped like a cone that is beside the object shaped like a cube. Use the words *next to* and *beside* to name the position of other shapes.

© Houghton Mifflin Harcourt Publishing Company

Chapter 10

six hundred twenty-five **625**

Lesson Check

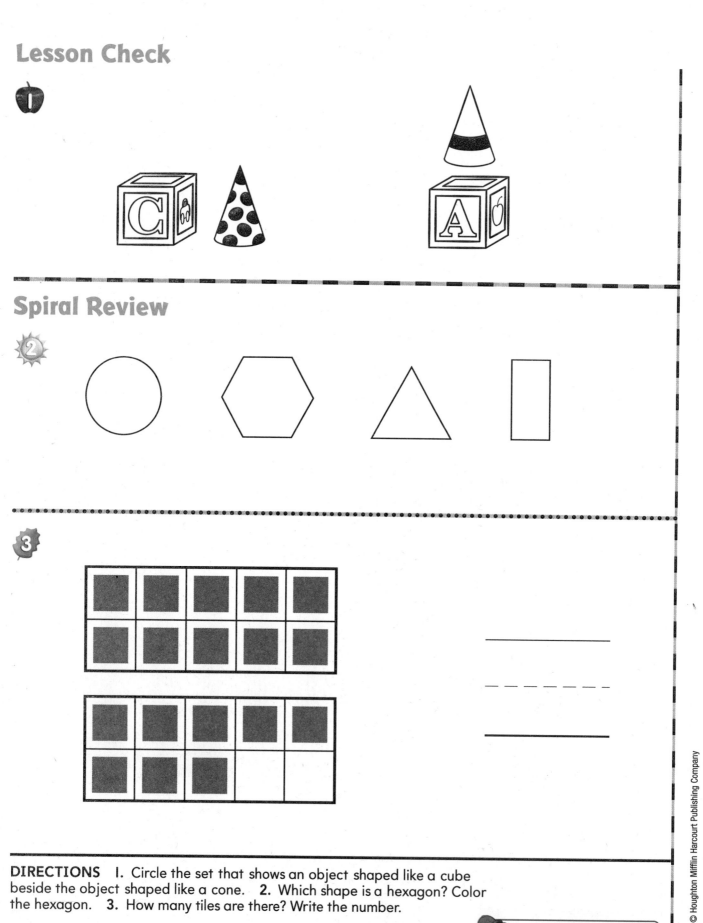

Spiral Review

DIRECTIONS   1. Circle the set that shows an object shaped like a cube beside the object shaped like a cone.   2. Which shape is a hexagon? Color the hexagon.   3. How many tiles are there? Write the number.

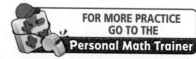

FOR MORE PRACTICE GO TO THE
Personal Math Trainer

Name _____

In Front Of and Behind

Essential Question How can you use the terms *in front of* and *behind* to describe shapes in the environment?

Learning Objective You will use the terms *in front of* and *behind* to describe the positions of objects in space.

DIRECTIONS Trace the X on the object shaped like a sphere that is in front of the object shaped like a cube. Trace the circle around the object shaped like a cylinder that is behind the object shaped like a cube.

Chapter 10 • Lesson 10

six hundred twenty-seven **627**

1

DIRECTIONS 1. Mark an X on the object shaped like a cylinder that is behind the object shaped like a cube. Draw a circle around the object shaped like a sphere that is directly in front of the object shaped like a cone. Use the words *in front of* and *behind* to name the position of other shapes.

628 six hundred twenty-eight

DIRECTIONS 2. Mark an X on the object shaped like a cube that is in front of the object shaped like a cylinder. Draw a circle around the object shaped like a cylinder that is behind the object shaped like a sphere. Use the words *in front of* and *behind* to name the position of other shaped objects.

Problem Solving • Applications

3

WRITE
Math

DIRECTIONS **3.** Draw or use pictures to show what you know about real world three-dimensional objects in front of and behind other objects.

HOME ACTIVITY • Tell your child you are thinking of something in the room that is in front of or behind another object. Have your child tell you the shape of the object.

Name _____

In Front Of and Behind

Learning Objective You will use the terms *in front of* and *behind* to describe the positions of objects in space.

1

DIRECTIONS I. Mark an X on the object shaped like a cylinder that is behind the object shaped like a cone. Draw a circle around the object shaped like a cylinder that is in front of the object shaped like a cube. Use the words *in front of* and *behind* to name the position of other shapes.

Chapter 10

six hundred thirty-one **631**

Lesson Check

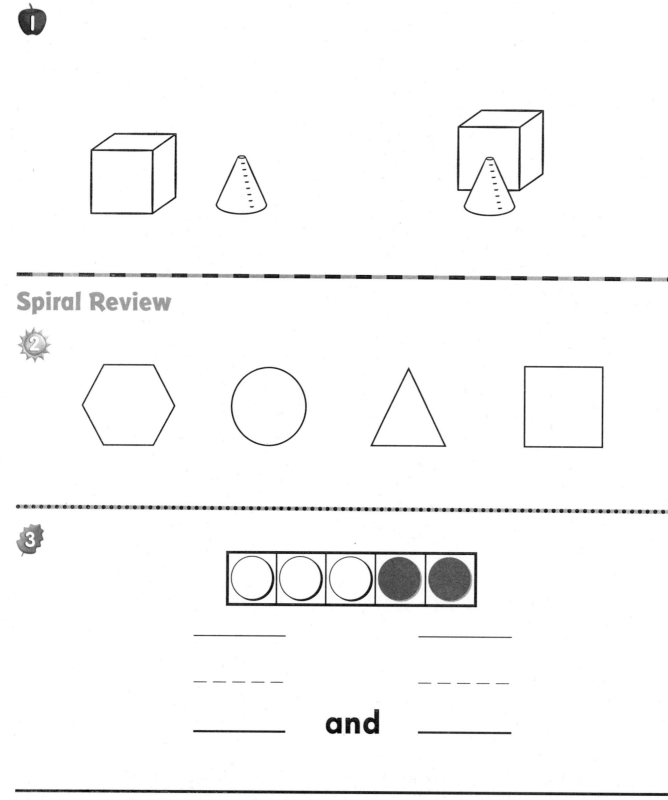

Spiral Review

and

DIRECTIONS **1.** Circle the set that shows an object shaped like a cone in front of the object shaped like a cube. **2.** Which shape is a triangle? Color the triangle. **3.** How many of each color counter? Write the numbers.

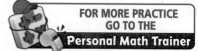

FOR MORE PRACTICE
GO TO THE
Personal Math Trainer

Name _____

Personal Math Trainer
Online Assessment
and Intervention

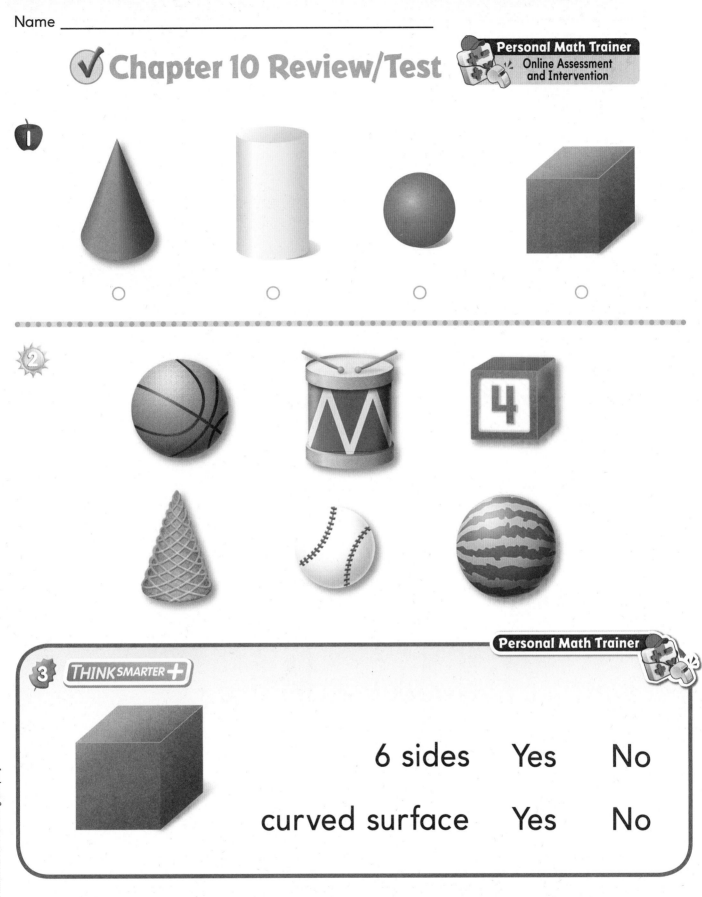

1

○   ○   ○   ○

2

Personal Math Trainer

3 THINK SMARTER +

6 sides	Yes	No
curved surface	Yes	No

© Houghton Mifflin Harcourt Publishing Company

DIRECTIONS 1. Mark under all the shapes that stack.   2. Which objects are shaped like a sphere? Mark an X on each of those objects.   3. Do the words describe a cube? Circle Yes or No.

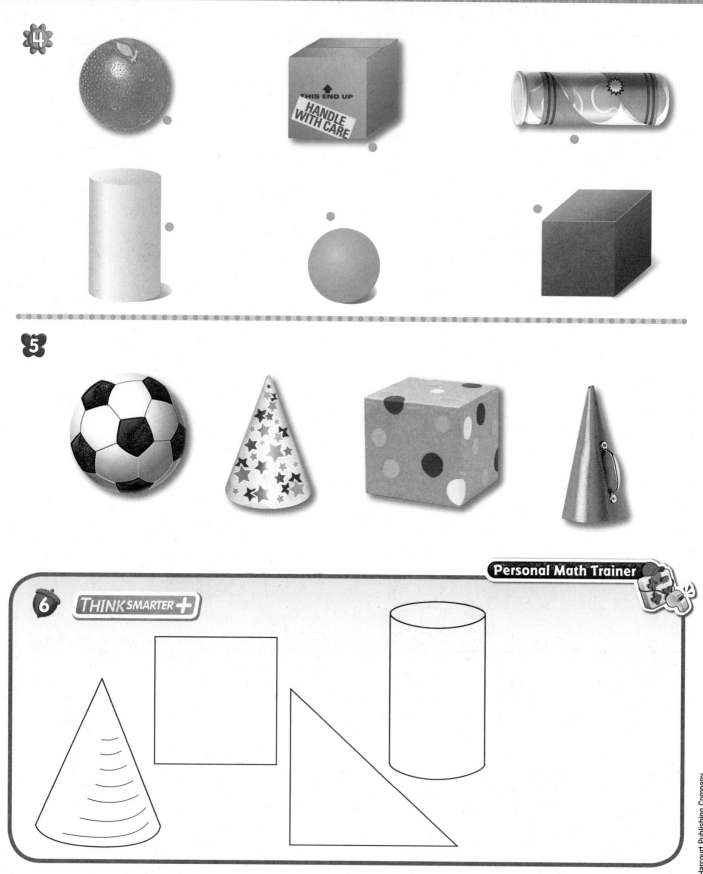

DIRECTIONS 4. Draw lines to match the objects to their shapes.
5. Which objects are shaped like a cone? Mark an X on each of those objects. **6.** Color the solid shapes blue. Color the flat shapes red. Draw another flat shape that is different.

Name _____

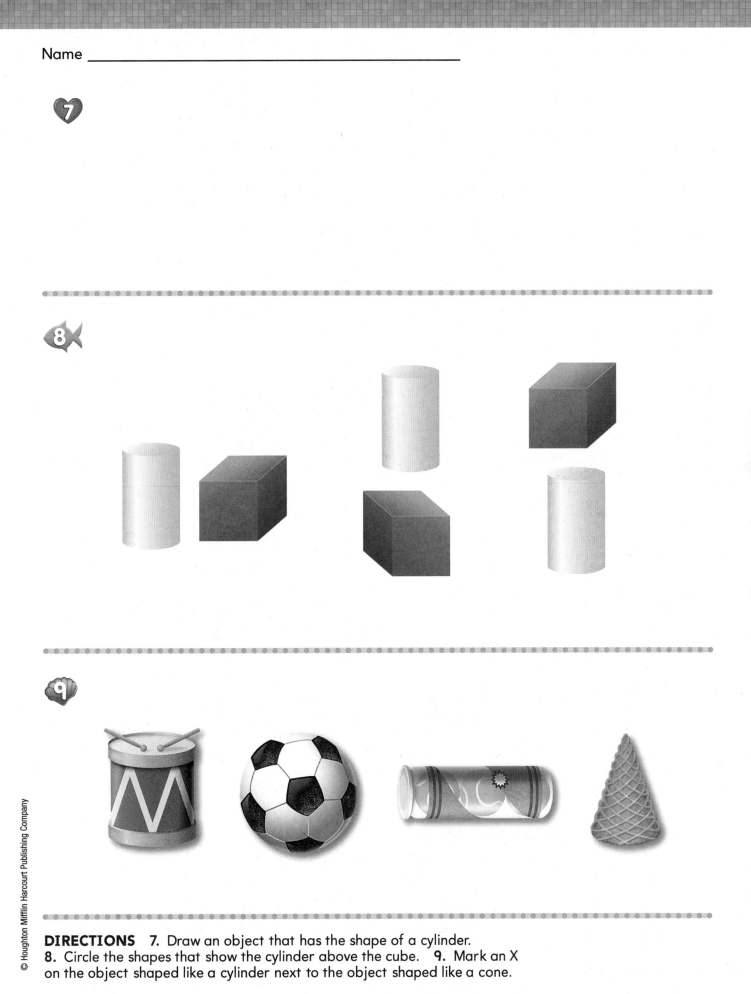

DIRECTIONS **7.** Draw an object that has the shape of a cylinder.
8. Circle the shapes that show the cylinder above the cube. **9.** Mark an X
on the object shaped like a cylinder next to the object shaped like a cone.

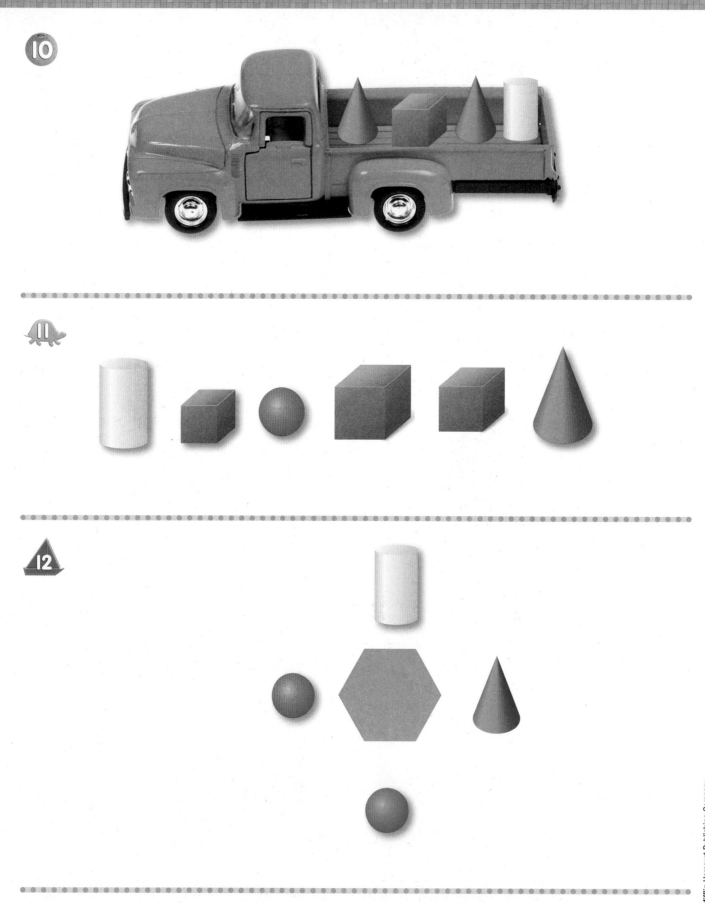

DIRECTIONS 10. Mark an X on the cone in front of the cube. 11. Mark an X on the cube that is beside the cone. 12. Mark an X on the sphere that is below the hexagon.

Plants all Around

written by Tami Morton

BIG IDEA Develop a conceptual understanding of measurement and data. Classify and count by color, shape, and size.

Two leaves fall from a tree.

Circle the leaf that is longer.

Science

Why do plants have leaves?

Two flowers grow near a wall.

Circle the flower that is shorter.

Science

Why do plants have flowers?

These carrots grow under the ground.

Circle the carrot that is longer.

Science

Why do plants have roots?

Cattails can be short or tall.

Circle the two cattails that are about the same height.

© Houghton Mifflin Harcourt Publishing Company • Image Credits: © Guenter Fischer/imagebroker/Alamy

Science

Why do plants have stems?

One leaf is shorter than the other leaf.

Draw a leaf that is about the same length as the shorter leaf.

Science

How are all these plants the same?

Write About the Story

Draw a purple flower. Make it shorter than the orange flower and taller than the yellow flower.

Vocabulary Review

longer   taller

shorter   same

Longer and Shorter

1. Look at the carrot. Draw a shorter carrot on the left.
Draw a longer carrot on the right.

2. Look at the leaf.
Draw a longer leaf
above it.
Draw a shorter leaf
below it.

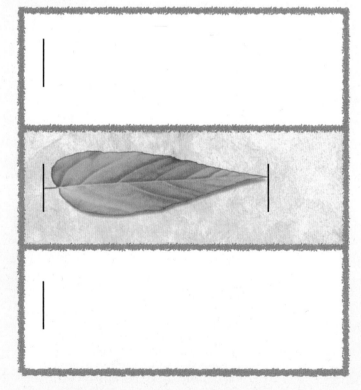

Measurement

Curious About Math with Curious George

A playground is an area designed for children to play.

• Which person on the park bench is bigger?

Name _____

✓ Show What You Know

Personal Math Trainer
Online Assessment and Intervention

More and Fewer

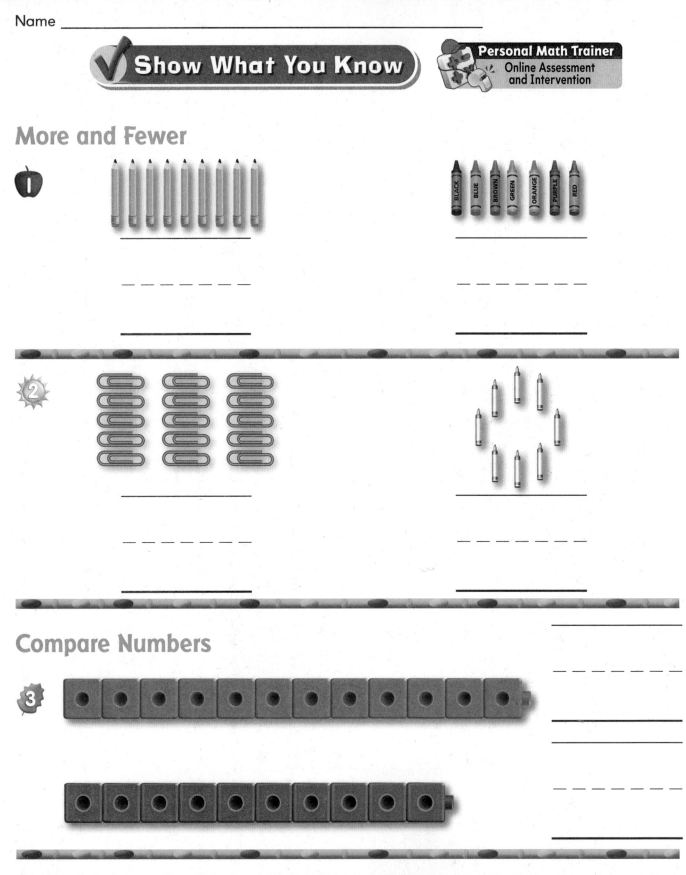

Compare Numbers

This page checks understanding of important skills needed for success in Chapter 11.

DIRECTIONS 1. Write how many in each set. Circle the set with fewer objects. 2. Write how many in each set. Circle the set with more objects. 3. Write how many cubes in each set. Circle the greater number.

646 six hundred forty-six

© Houghton Mifflin Harcourt Publishing Company

Name _____

bigger

smaller

DIRECTIONS Are there more flowers in the bigger pot or the smaller pot? Circle to show the pot with more flowers.

GO DIGITAL
• Interactive Student Edition
• Multimedia eGlossary

Game

Connecting Cube Challenge

DIRECTIONS Take turns with a partner tossing the number cube. Move your marker that number of spaces. If a player lands on a cube, he or she takes a cube for making a cube train. At the end of the game, players compare cube trains. Each player identifies the number of cubes in his or her cube train. If one player has a greater number of cubes, partners should identify that as the larger quantity of cubes.

MATERIALS game markers, number cube (1–6), connecting cubes

heavier más pesado 33	**lighter** más liviano 39
longer más largo 40	**same height** de la misma altura 55
same length del mismo largo 56	**same weight** del mismo peso 58
shorter más corto 62	**taller** más alto 73

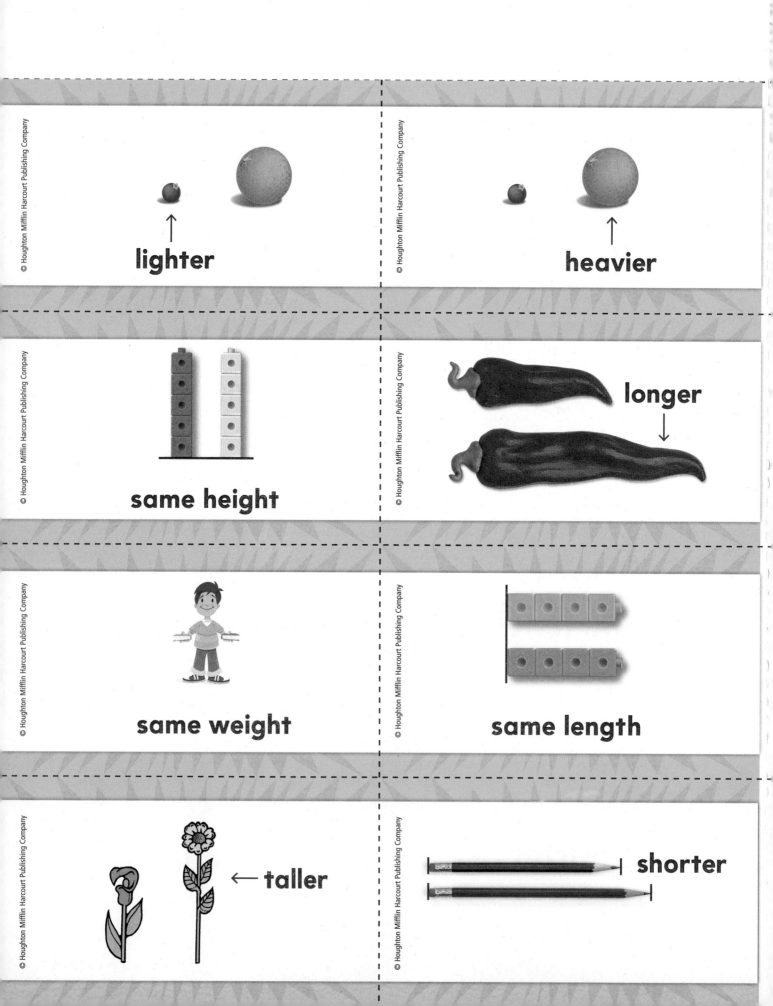

lighter

heavier

same height

longer

same weight

same length

taller

shorter

Measurement

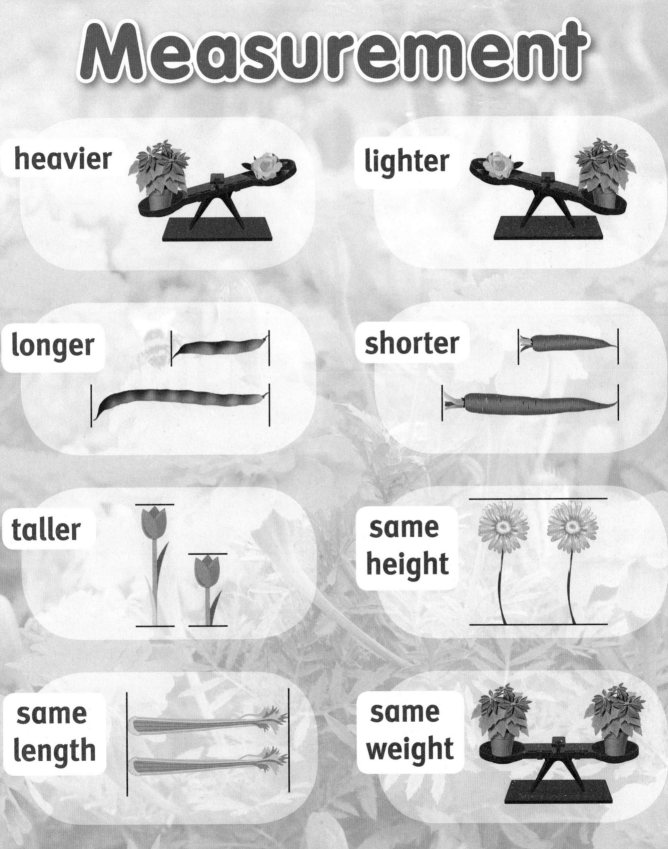

heavier

lighter

longer

shorter

taller

same height

same length

same weight

DIRECTIONS Say each word. Tell something you know about the word.

heavier

weight

same

shorter

FINISH

same
length

DIRECTIONS Place game pieces on START. Play with a partner. Take turns. Toss the number cube. Move that many spaces. If a player lands on a space with a word or words, he or she uses connecting cubes to model and tell about the word. If the model is correct, the player gets 1 point. When a player has 5 points, follow the closest green path to FINISH. The first player to reach FINISH wins.

MATERIALS 2-color counter game piece for each player, number cube, red and blue connecting cubes

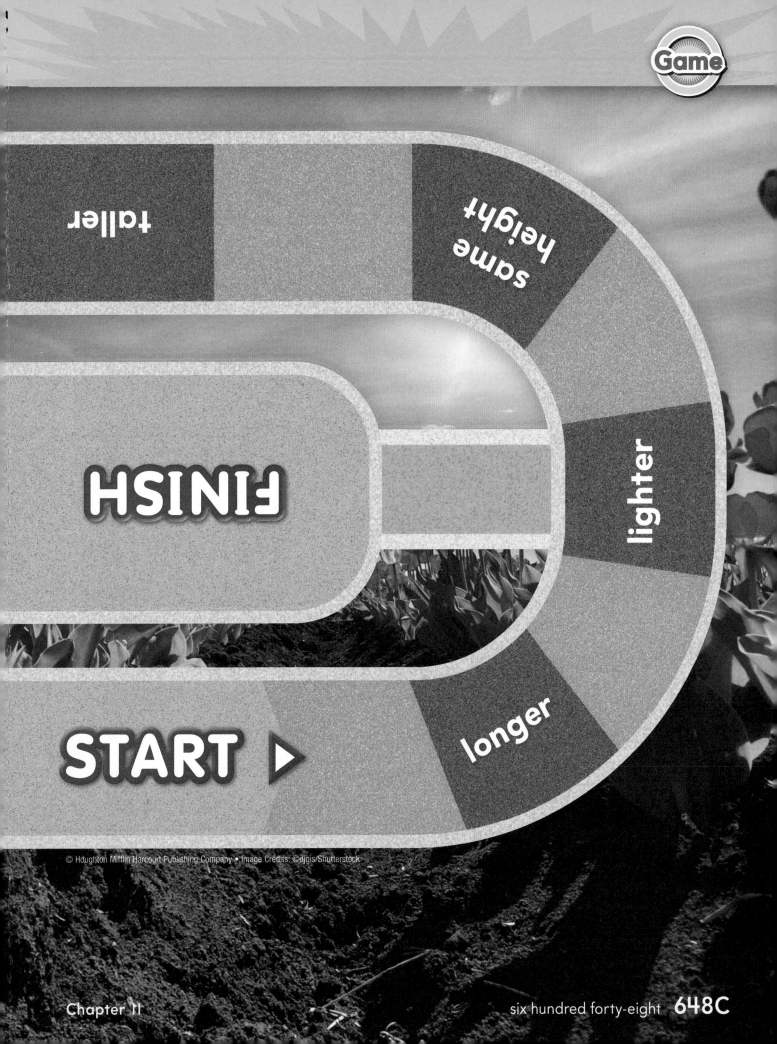

taller

same height

lighter

FINISH

longer

START ▶

The Write Way

DIRECTIONS Draw to show how to compare the length of two objects.
Reflect Be ready to tell about your drawing.

© Houghton Mifflin Harcourt Publishing Company • Image Credits: ©Olena Mykhaylova/Shutterstock

Name _____

Compare Lengths

Essential Question How can you compare the lengths of two objects?

Learning Objective You will make a direct comparison of the lengths of two objects.

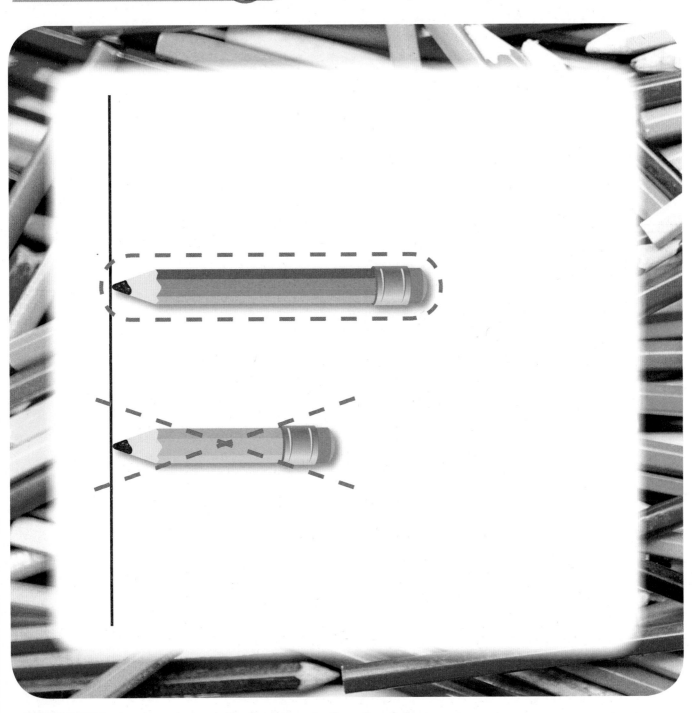

DIRECTIONS Look at the pencils. Compare the lengths of the two pencils. Use the words *longer than*, *shorter than*, or *about the same length* to describe the lengths. Trace the circle around the longer pencil. Trace the X on the shorter pencil.

Chapter 11 • Lesson 1

© Houghton Mifflin Harcourt Publishing Company • Image Credits: (bg) ©Corbis Premium RF/Alamy

Share and Show

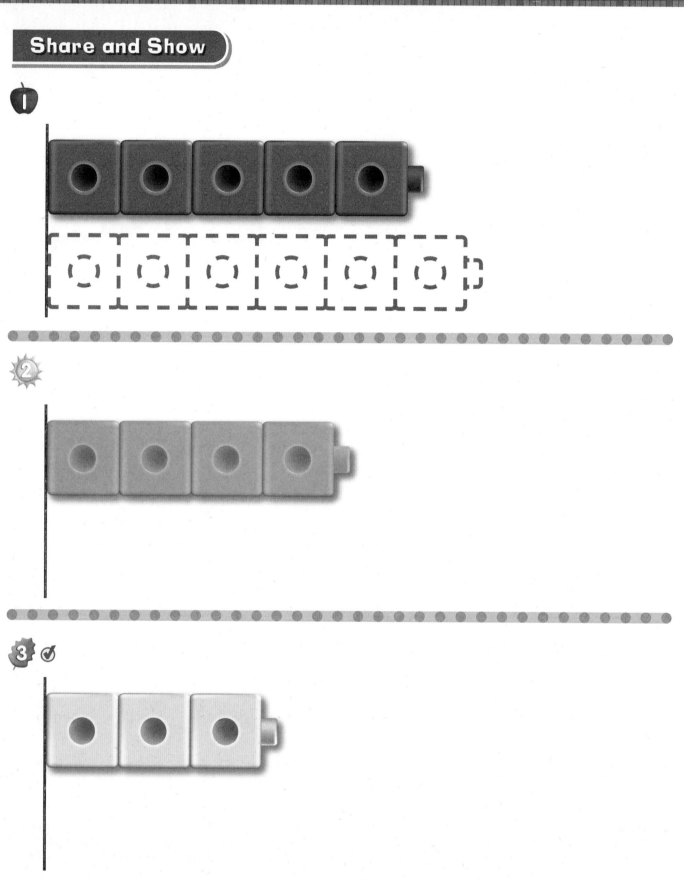

1

2

3 ☑

DIRECTIONS 1. Place cubes on the longer cube train. Trace and color the cube train. **2–3.** Make a cube train that is longer than the cube train shown. Draw and color the cube train.

650 six hundred fifty

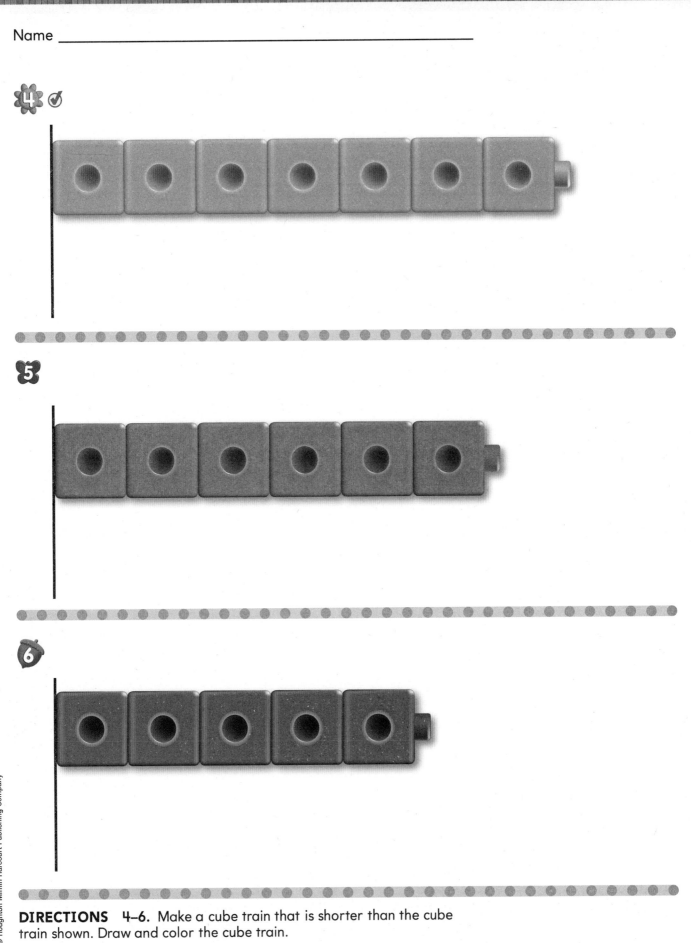

DIRECTIONS 4–6. Make a cube train that is shorter than the cube train shown. Draw and color the cube train.

Problem Solving • Applications

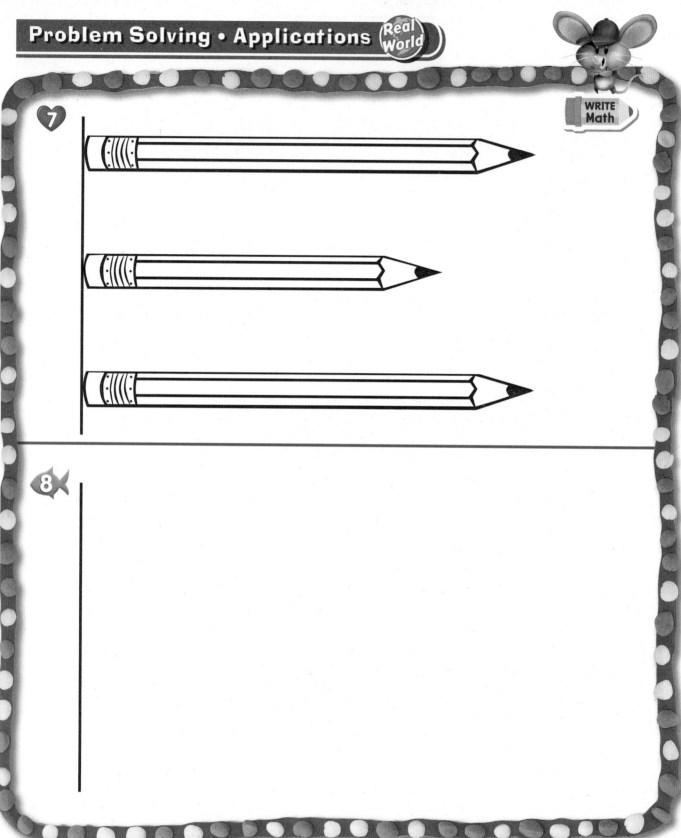

DIRECTIONS 7. Two of these pencils are about the same length. Color those pencils. **8.** Draw to show what you know about two objects that are about the same length. Tell a friend about your drawing.

HOME ACTIVITY • Show your child a pencil and ask him or her to find an object that is longer than the pencil. Repeat with an object that is shorter than the pencil.

Name _____

Compare Lengths

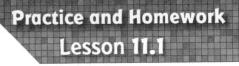

Practice and Homework
Lesson 11.1

Learning Objective You will make a direct comparison of the lengths of two objects.

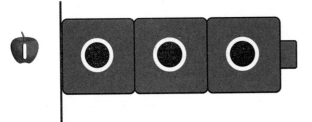

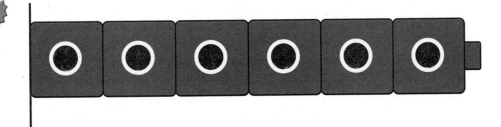

DIRECTIONS **1.** Make a cube train that is longer than the cube train shown. Draw and color the cube train. **2.** Make a cube train that is shorter than the cube train shown. Draw and color the cube train. **3.** Make a cube train that is about the same length as the cube train shown. Draw and color the cube train.

© Houghton Mifflin Harcourt Publishing Company

Chapter 11

six hundred fifty-three **653**

Lesson Check

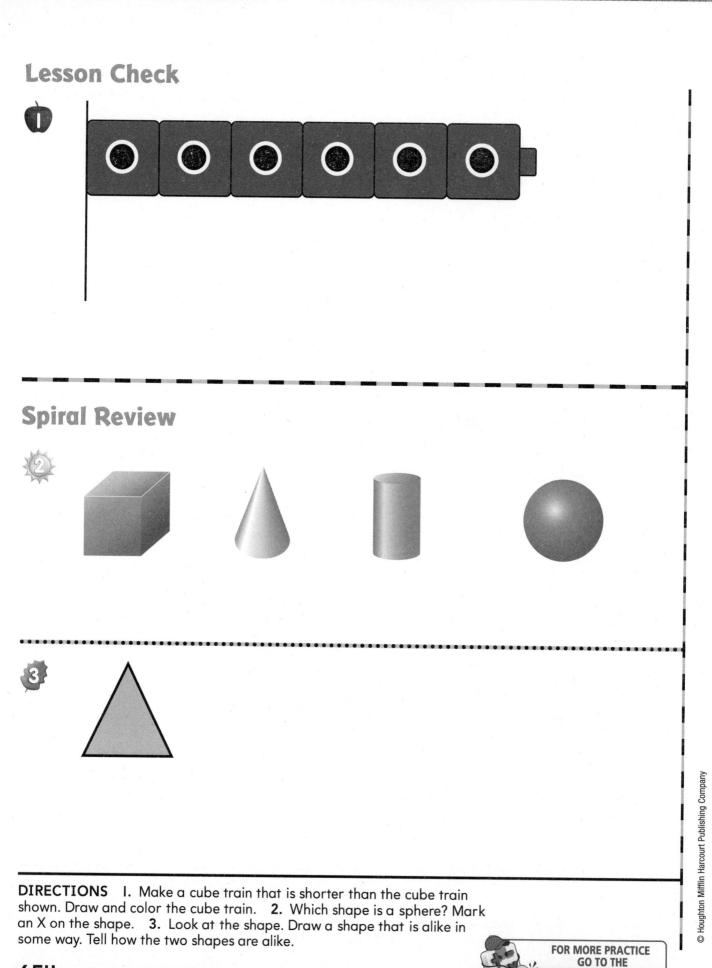

1

Spiral Review

2

3

DIRECTIONS **1.** Make a cube train that is shorter than the cube train shown. Draw and color the cube train. **2.** Which shape is a sphere? Mark an X on the shape. **3.** Look at the shape. Draw a shape that is alike in some way. Tell how the two shapes are alike.

654 six hundred fifty-four

**FOR MORE PRACTICE
GO TO THE
Personal Math Trainer**

Name _____

Compare Heights

Essential Question How can you compare
the heights of two objects?

Learning Objective You will make a
direct comparison of the heights of two
objects.

 Listen and Draw *Real World*

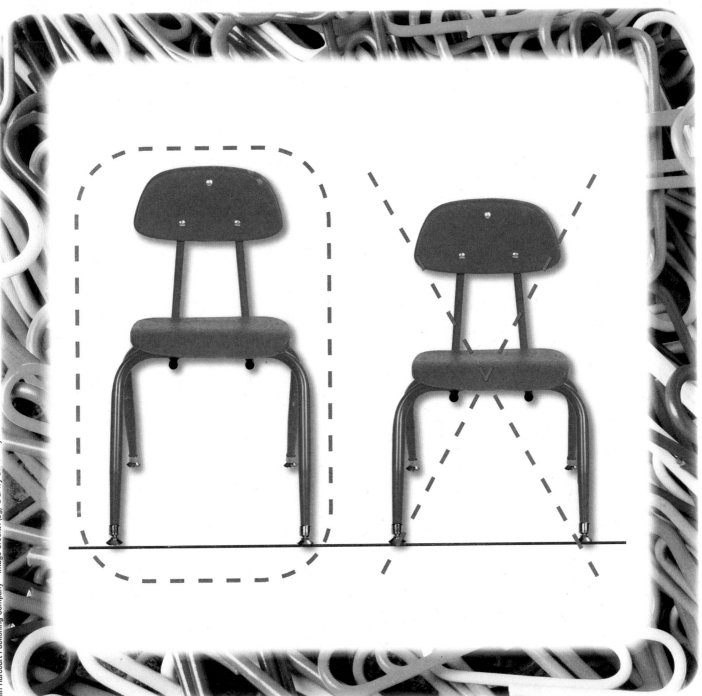

DIRECTIONS Look at the chairs. Compare the heights of the two
chairs. Use the words *taller than*, *shorter than*, or *about the same height*
to describe the heights. Trace the circle around the taller chair. Trace
the X on the shorter chair.

Chapter 11 • Lesson 2

six hundred fifty-five **655**

© Houghton Mifflin Harcourt Publishing Company • Image Credit: (bg) ©Gerry Gavery ...my

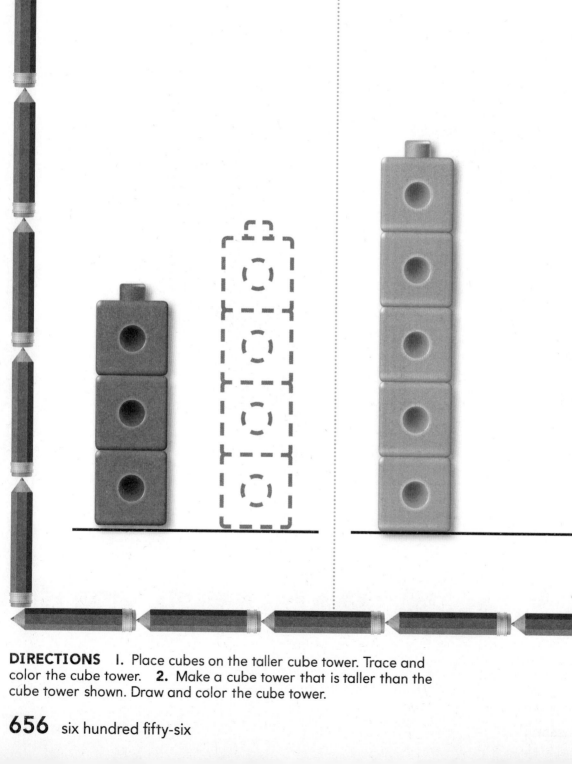

DIRECTIONS 1. Place cubes on the taller cube tower. Trace and color the cube tower. 2. Make a cube tower that is taller than the cube tower shown. Draw and color the cube tower.

Name _____

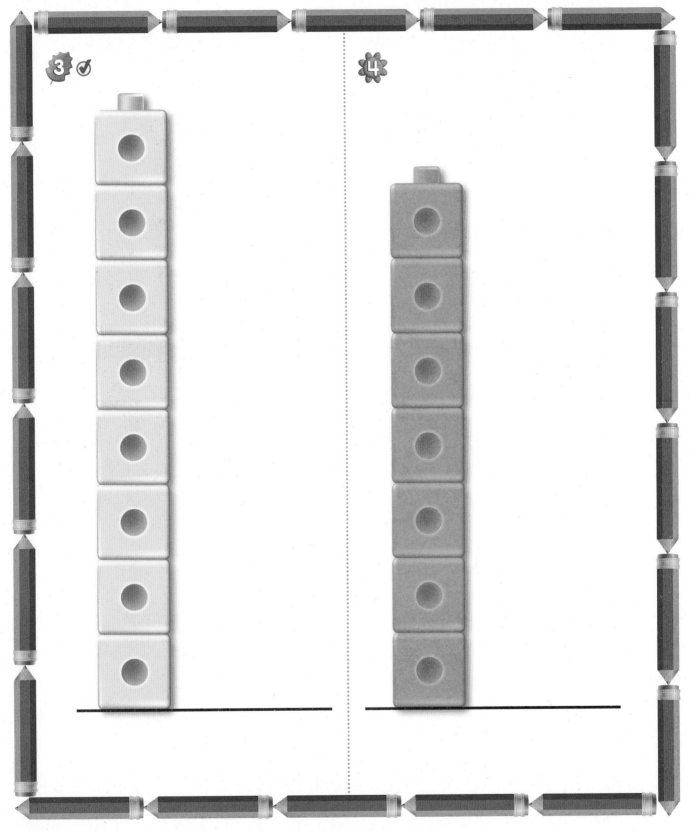

DIRECTIONS 3–4. Make a cube tower that is shorter than the cube tower shown. Draw and color the cube tower.

six hundred fifty-seven **657**

Problem Solving • Applications *Real World*

5

WRITE Math

6

DIRECTIONS **5.** Color the trees that are about the same height. **6.** Draw to show what you know about two cube towers that are about the same height. Tell a friend about your drawing.

HOME ACTIVITY • Have your child find two objects, such as plastic toys or stuffed animals. Have him or her place the objects side by side to compare the heights. Ask your child which object is taller and which object is shorter.

Name _____

Compare Heights

Learning Objective You will make a direct comparison of the heights of two objects.

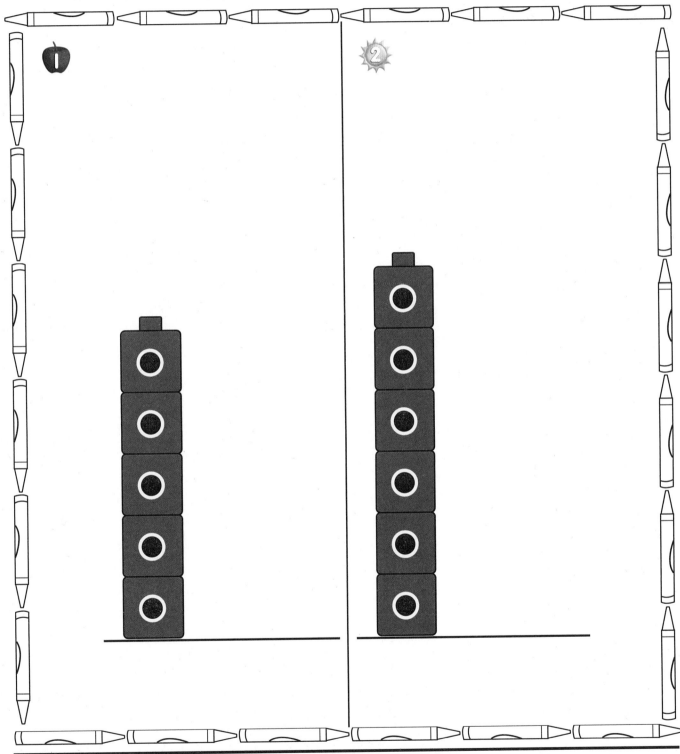

DIRECTIONS **1.** Make a cube tower that is taller than the cube tower shown. Draw and color the cube tower. **2.** Make a cube tower that is shorter than the cube tower shown. Draw and color the cube tower.

Chapter 11

six hundred fifty-nine **659**

Lesson Check

1

Spiral Review

2

CAT
TOYS

3

$$5 - \underline{} = 2$$

DIRECTIONS 1. Make a cube tower that is shorter than the cube tower shown. Draw and color the cube tower. 2. Circle the set that shows an object shaped like a sphere below the object shaped like a cube. 3. How many are being taken from the set? Write the number.

**FOR MORE PRACTICE
GO TO THE
Personal Math Trainer**

Name _____

Problem Solving • Direct Comparison

Essential Question How can you solve problems using the strategy *draw a picture?*

Learning Objective You will use the strategy *draw a picture* by comparing the lengths or heights of objects to solve problems.

DIRECTIONS Compare the lengths or heights of two classroom objects. Draw the objects. Tell a friend about your drawing.

Chapter 11 • Lesson 3

1

DIRECTIONS 1. Find two small classroom objects. Place one end of each object on the line. Compare the lengths. Draw the objects. Say *longer than*, *shorter than*, or *about the same length* to describe the lengths. Circle both objects if they are about the same length. Circle the longer object if one object is longer than the other.

Name _____

② ✓

DIRECTIONS **2.** Find two small classroom objects. Place one end of each object on the line. Compare the heights. Draw the objects. Say *taller than*, *shorter than*, or *about the same height* to describe the heights. Circle both objects if they are about the same height. Circle the shorter object if one object is shorter than the other.

HOME ACTIVITY • Show your child two objects of different lengths. Have him or her put the ends of the objects on a straight line to compare the lengths and tell which object is shorter and which object is longer.

Personal Math Trainer
Online Assessment
and Intervention

Concepts and Skills

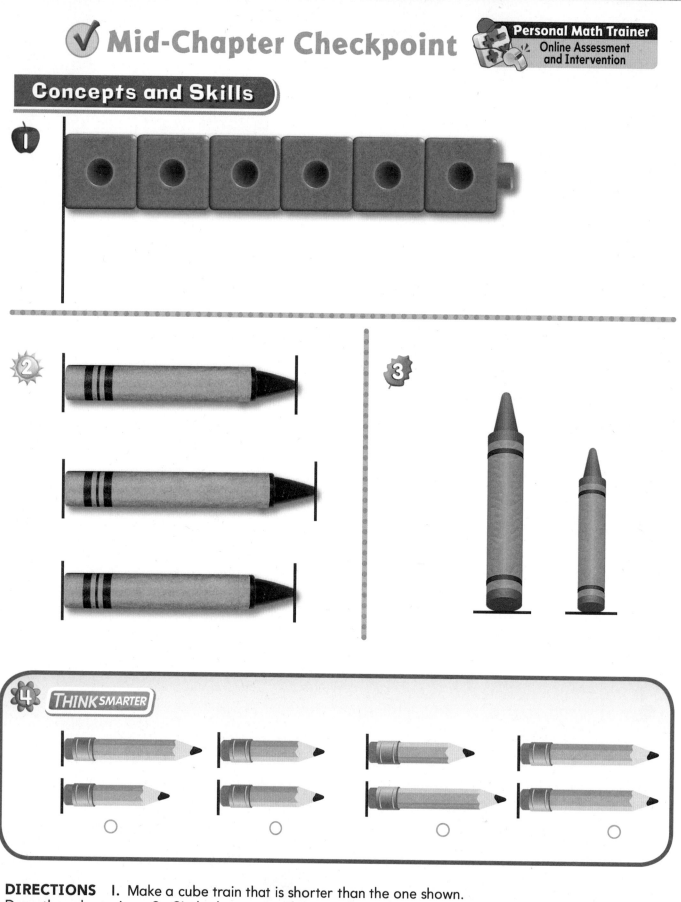

DIRECTIONS 1. Make a cube train that is shorter than the one shown. Draw the cube train. 2. Circle the crayons that are about the same length. 3. Circle the crayon that is shorter. 4. Choose all the sets with two pencils that are about the same length.

Name _____

Problem Solving • Direct Comparison

Learning Objective You will use the strategy *draw a picture* by comparing the lengths or heights of objects to solve problems.

DIRECTIONS **I.** Find two small classroom objects. Place one end of each object on the line. Compare the lengths. Draw the objects. Say *longer than*, *shorter than*, or *about the same length* to describe the lengths. Circle both objects if they are about the same length. Circle the longer object if one object is longer than the other. **2.** Find two small classroom objects. Place one end of each object on the line. Compare the heights. Draw the objects. Say *taller than*, *shorter than*, or *about the same height* to describe the heights. Circle both objects if they are about the same height. Circle the shorter object if one object is shorter than the other.

Lesson Check

🍎 1

Spiral Review

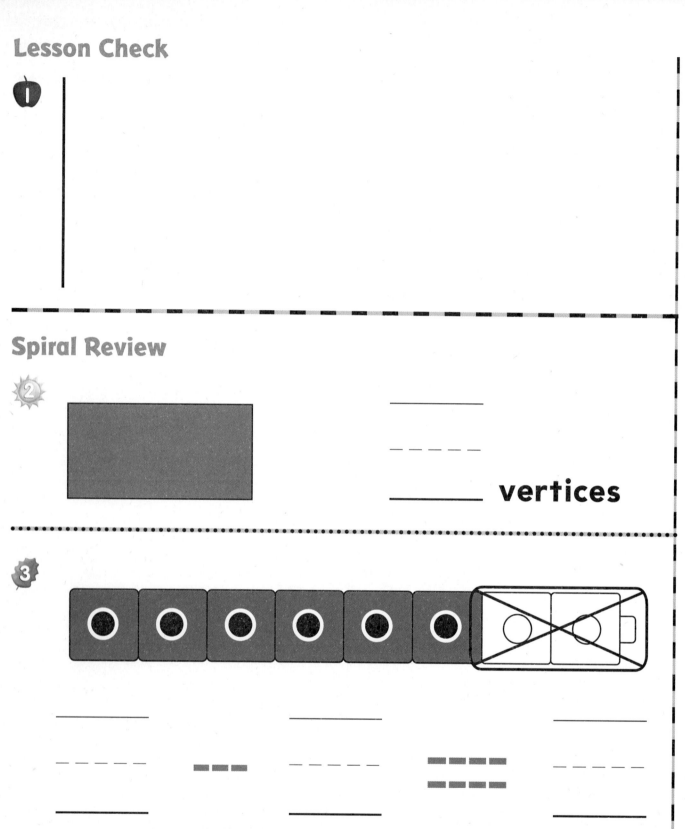

_____

- - - - - - -

_____ **vertices**

_____   _____   _____

- - - - - - -   ▬▬ ▬▬   - - - - -   ▬▬ ▬▬   - - - - -
                                       ▬▬ ▬▬

_____   _____   _____

DIRECTIONS 1. Find two pencils. Place one end of each pencil on the line. Compare the lengths. Draw the pencils. Say *longer than*, *shorter than*, or *about the same length* to describe the lengths. Circle both pencils if they are about the same length. Circle the shorter pencil if one pencil is shorter than the other. 2. How many vertices does the rectangle have? Write the number. 3. Use the cubes to complete the subtraction sentence.

666 six hundred sixty-six

FOR MORE PRACTICE GO TO THE
Personal Math Trainer

Name _____

Compare Weights

Essential Question How can you compare the weights of two objects?

Learning Objective You will make a direct comparison of the weights of two objects.

DIRECTIONS Look at the picture. Compare the weights of the two objects. Use the words *heavier than*, *lighter than*, or *about the same weight* to describe the weights. Trace the circle around the lighter object. Trace the X on the heavier object.

Chapter 11 • Lesson 4

six hundred sixty-seven **667**

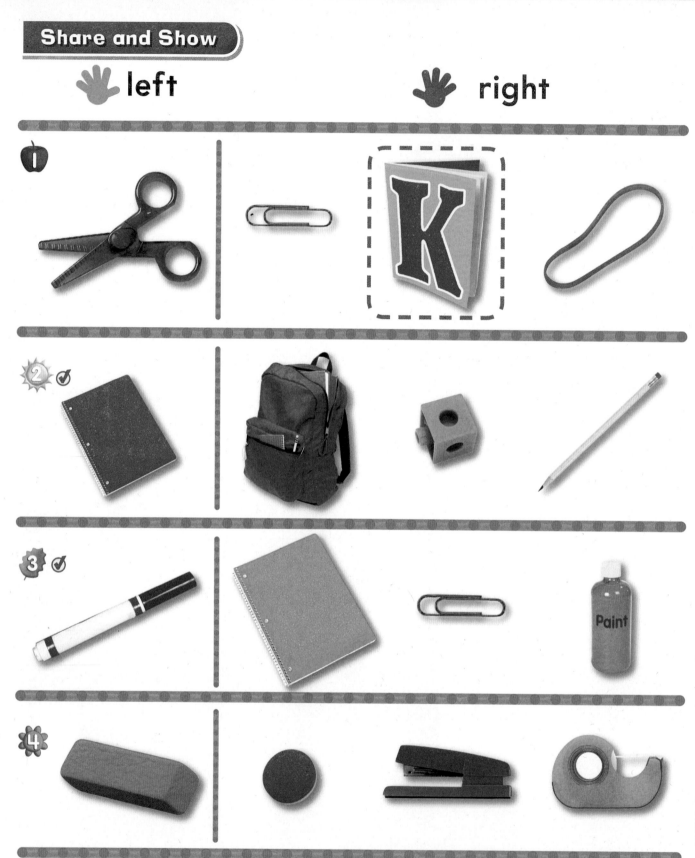

👋 left   👋 right

DIRECTIONS Find the first object in the row, and hold it in your left hand. Find the rest of the objects in the row, and take turns holding each of the objects in your right hand. **1.** Trace to show the object that is heavier than the object in your left hand. **2.** Circle the object that is heavier than the object in your left hand. **3–4.** Circle the object that is lighter than the object in your left hand.

Name _____

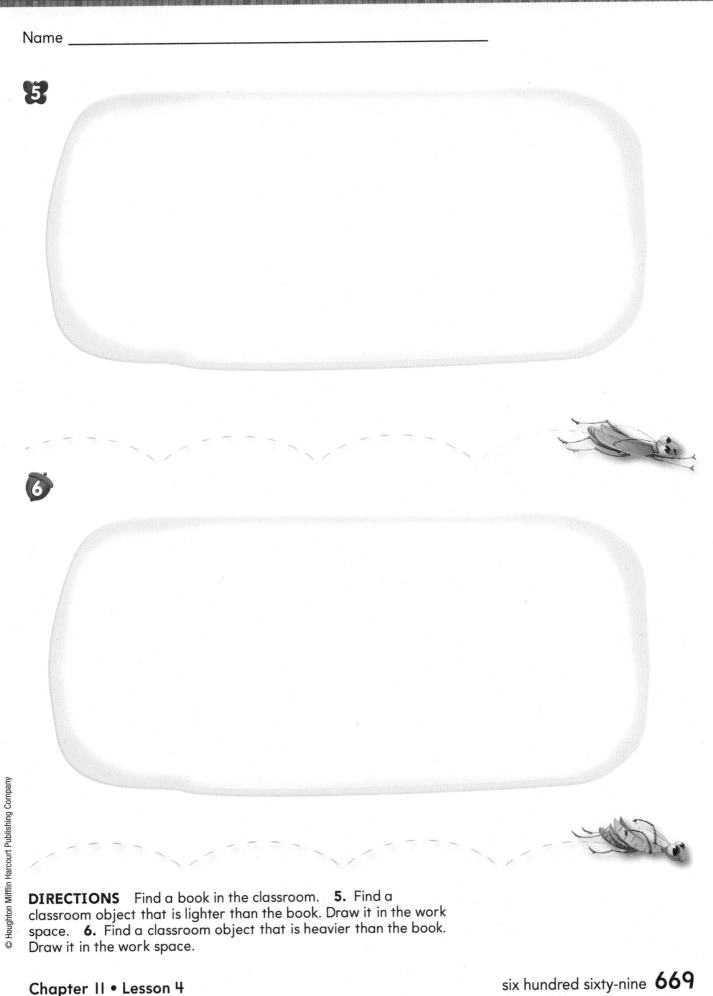

5

6

DIRECTIONS Find a book in the classroom. **5.** Find a classroom object that is lighter than the book. Draw it in the work space. **6.** Find a classroom object that is heavier than the book. Draw it in the work space.

Chapter 11 • Lesson 4

six hundred sixty-nine **669**

© Houghton Mifflin Harcourt Publishing Company

Problem Solving • Applications

7

WRITE
Math

DIRECTIONS   7. Draw to show what you know about comparing the weights of two objects. Tell a friend about your drawing.

HOME ACTIVITY • Have your child compare the weights of two objects in a house. Then have him or her use the terms *heavier* and *lighter* to describe the weights.

Name _____

Compare Weights

Learning Objective You will make a direct comparison of the weights of two objects.

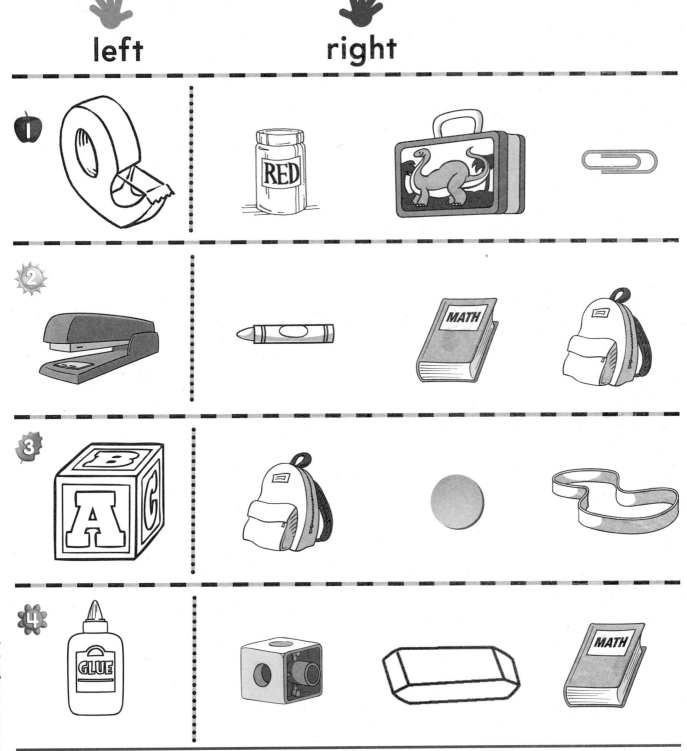

left   right

DIRECTIONS Find the first object in the row, and hold it in your left hand. Find the rest of the objects in the row, and hold each object in your right hand.   **1–2.** Circle the object that is lighter than the object in your left hand.   **3–4.** Circle the object that is heavier than the object in your left hand.

Lesson Check

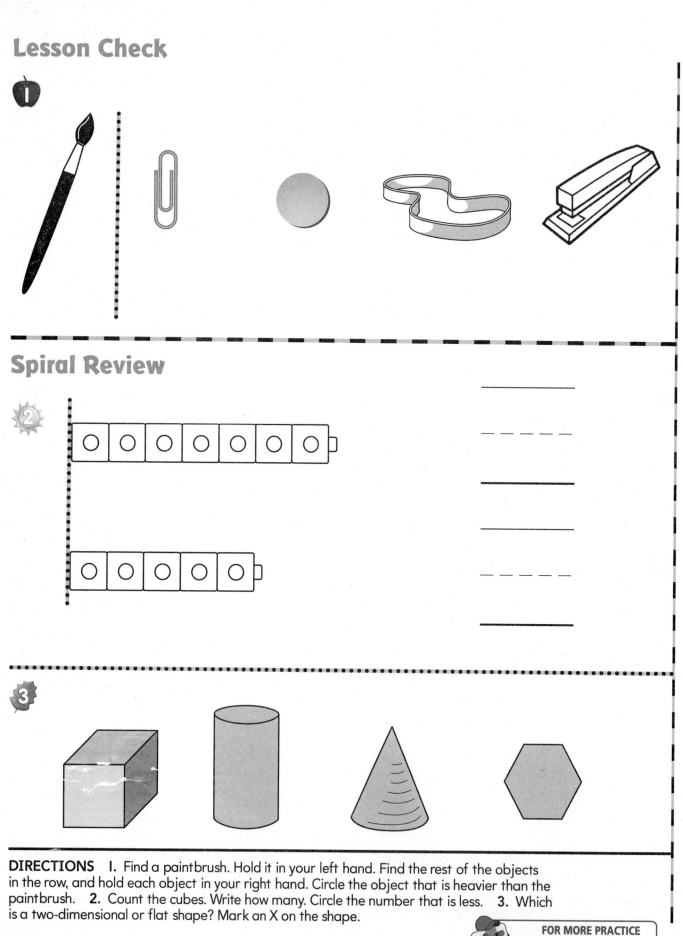

1

Spiral Review

2

3

DIRECTIONS **1.** Find a paintbrush. Hold it in your left hand. Find the rest of the objects in the row, and hold each object in your right hand. Circle the object that is heavier than the paintbrush. **2.** Count the cubes. Write how many. Circle the number that is less. **3.** Which is a two-dimensional or flat shape? Mark an X on the shape.

672 six hundred seventy-two

**FOR MORE PRACTICE
GO TO THE
Personal Math Trainer**

Name _____

Length, Height, and Weight

Essential Question How can you describe several ways to measure one object?

Learning Objective You will describe several ways to measure one object.

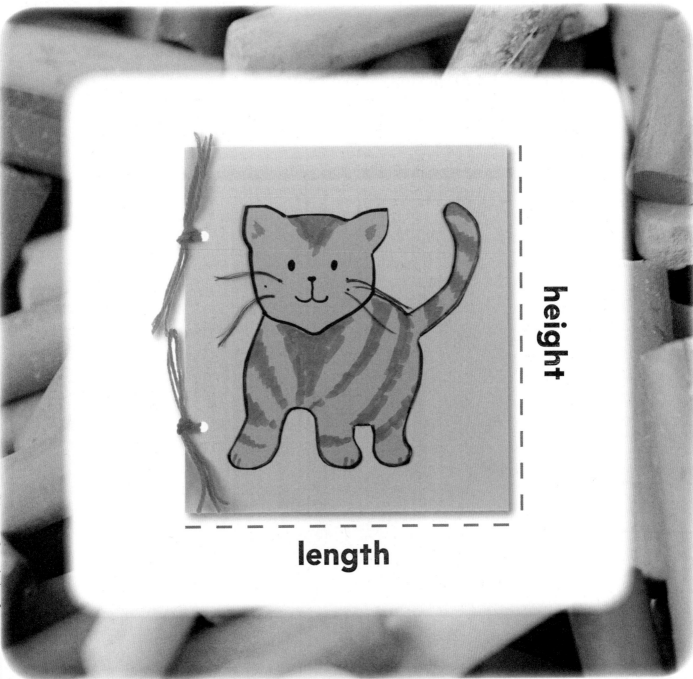

height

length

DIRECTIONS Look at the book. Trace your finger over the line that shows how to measure the height of the book. Trace your finger over the line that shows how to measure the length of the book. Talk about another way to measure the book.

Chapter 11 • Lesson 5

six hundred seventy-three **673**

© Houghton Mifflin Harcourt Publishing Company • Image Credits: (bg) ©Corbis Premium RF/Alamy

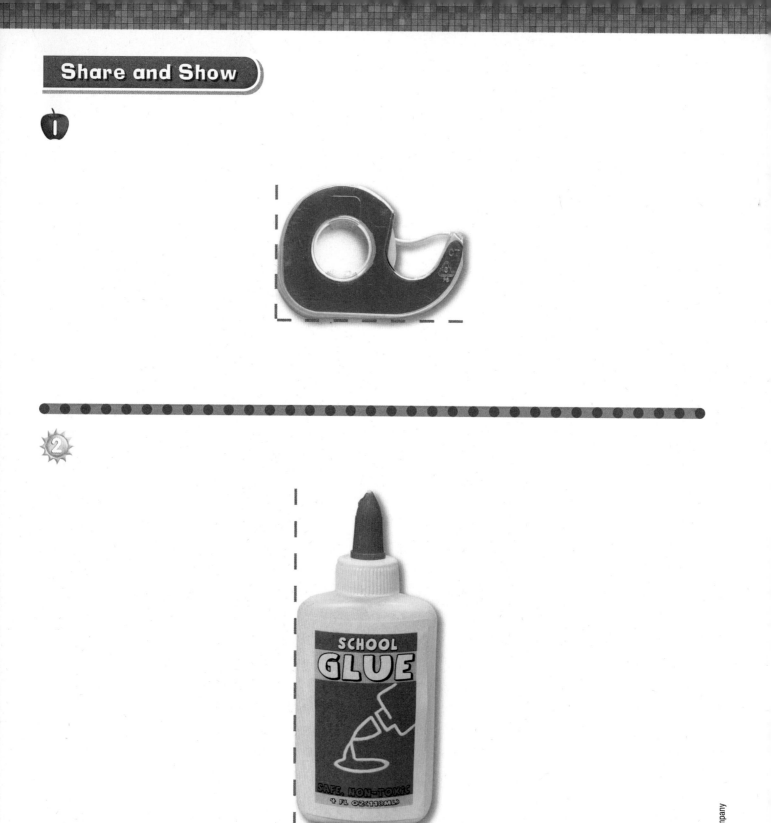

Share and Show

1

2

DIRECTIONS 1–2. Use red to trace the line that shows how to measure the length. Use blue to trace the line that shows how to measure the height. Talk about another way to measure the object.

674 six hundred seventy-four

© Houghton Mifflin Harcourt Publishing Company

Name _____

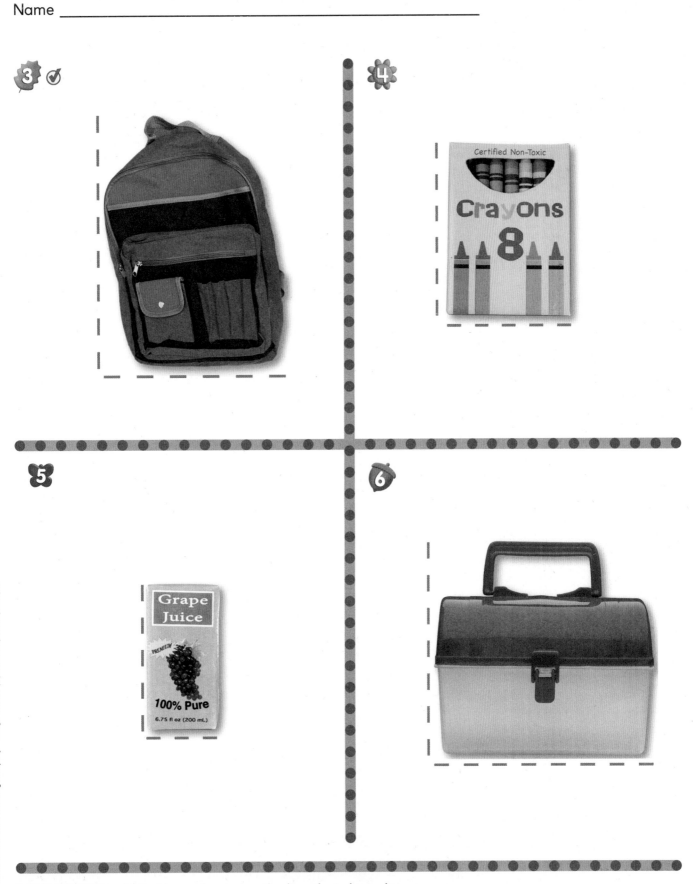

DIRECTIONS 3–6. Use red to trace the line that shows how to measure the length. Use blue to trace the line that shows how to measure the height. Talk about another way to measure the object.

Problem Solving • Applications

7

WRITE
Math

DIRECTIONS   7. Draw to show what you know about measuring an object in more than one way.

HOME ACTIVITY • Show your child an object in the house that can be easily measured by length, height, and weight. Ask him or her to describe the different ways to measure the object.

Length, Height, and Weight

Learning Objective You will describe several ways to measure one object.

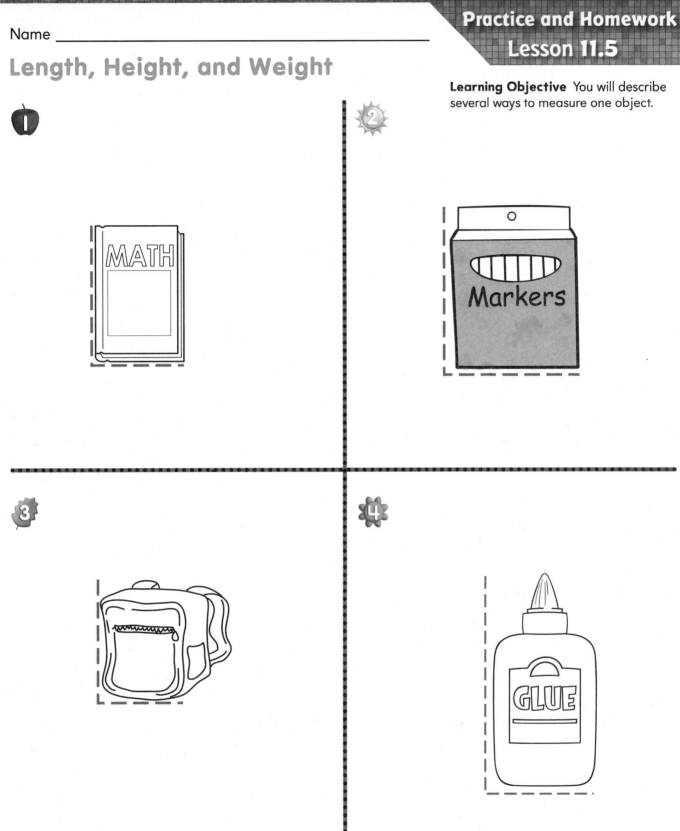

DIRECTIONS 1–4. Use red to trace the line that shows how to measure the length. Use blue to trace the line that shows how to measure the height. Talk about another way to measure the object.

Chapter 11

six hundred seventy-seven **677**

Lesson Check

1

Spiral Review

2

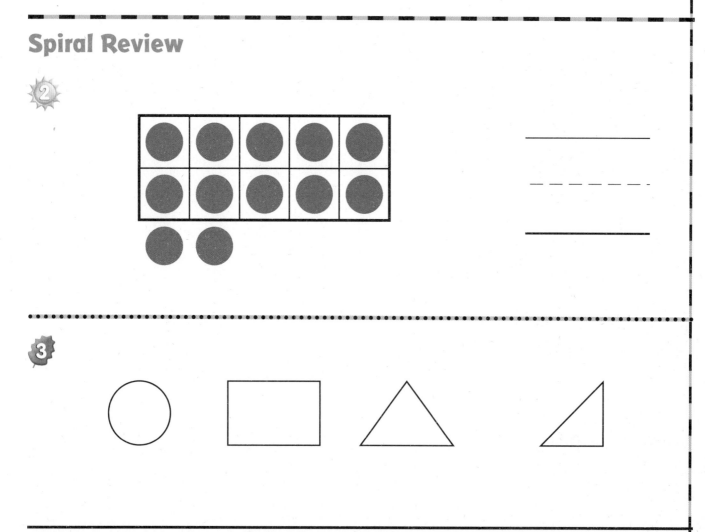

3

DIRECTIONS 1. Use red to trace the line that shows how to measure the length. Use blue to trace the line that shows how to measure the height. 2. Count and tell how many. Write the number. 3. Which shape is a rectangle? Color the rectangle.

678 six hundred seventy-eight

FOR MORE PRACTICE
GO TO THE
Personal Math Trainer

✓ Chapter 11 Review/Test

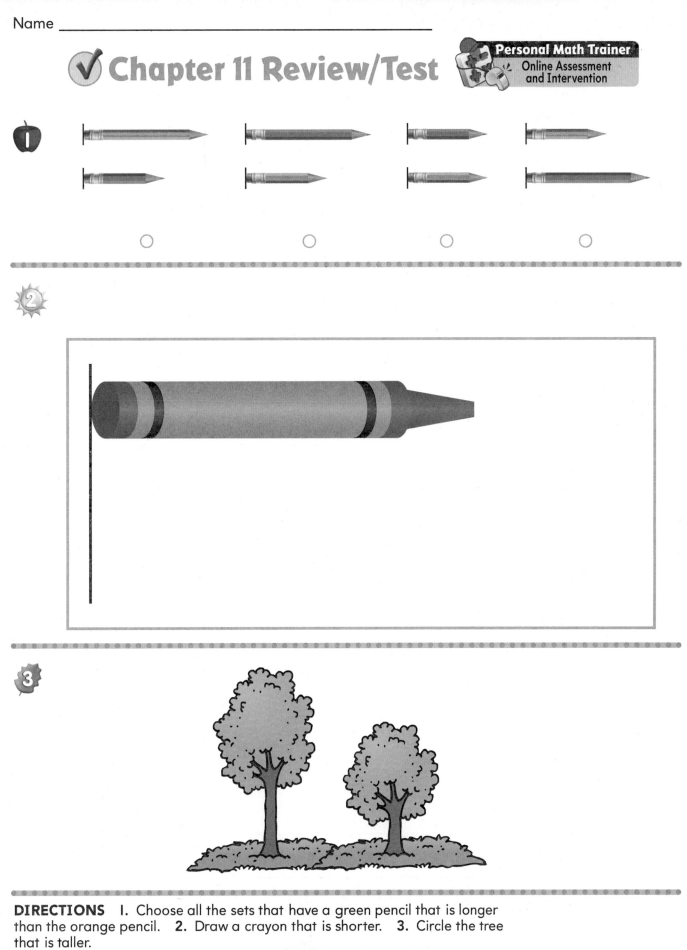

© Houghton Mifflin Harcourt Publishing Company

DIRECTIONS 1. Choose all the sets that have a green pencil that is longer than the orange pencil. 2. Draw a crayon that is shorter. 3. Circle the tree that is taller.

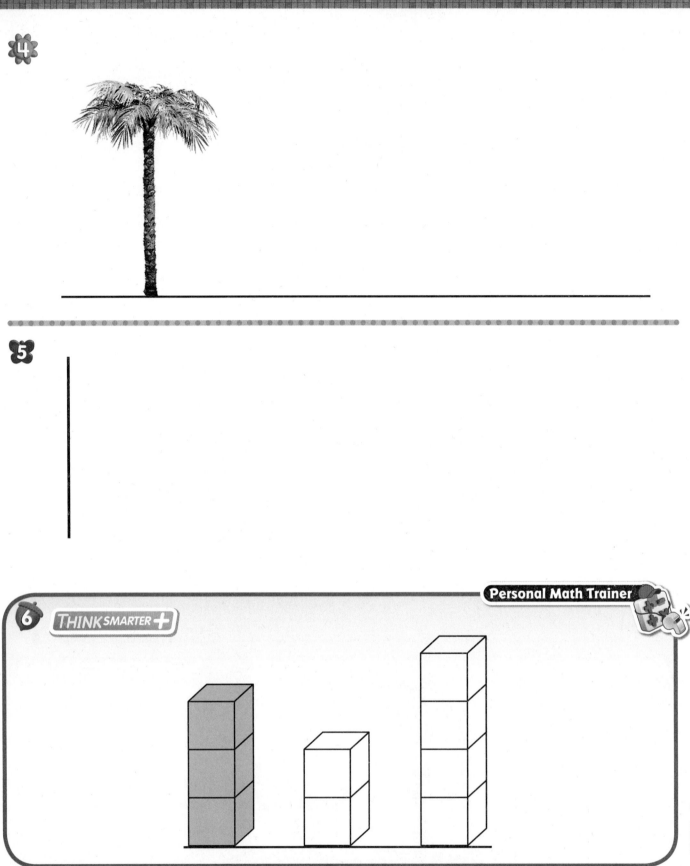

4

5

Personal Math Trainer

6 THINK SMARTER +

DIRECTIONS **4.** This tree is taller than another tree. Draw to show the other tree. **5.** Draw two pieces of yarn of different lengths. Draw a circle around the yarn that is longer. **6.** Which cube tower is shorter than the green cube tower? Color it blue. Which cube tower is taller than the green cube tower? Color it red.

Name _____

7

8

    ○ Yes   ○ No

    ○ Yes   ○ No

    ○ Yes   ○ No

Personal Math Trainer

9 THINK SMARTER +

Orange Juice — 100% Pure — 6.75 fl oz (200 ml)

DIRECTIONS **7.** Circle all the objects that are lighter than the book. **8.** Is the object heavier than the tape dispenser? Choose Yes or No. **9.** Draw a line to show the height of the juice box. Draw a line to show the length of the lunchbox.

© Houghton Mifflin Harcourt Publishing Company • Image Credits: (tcr) ©Artville/Getty Images; (br) ©Stockbyte/Getty Images; (tc) ©Siede Preis/PhotoDisc/Getty Images

○   ○   ○   ○

DIRECTIONS **10.** Choose all of the pictures that have lines that show how to measure height. **11.** Look at the objects. Mark an X on the lighter object. Circle the heavier object. **12.** Draw an object that is heavier than the pencil.

Classify and Sort Data

Curious About Math with
Curious George

Primary colors are blue, red, and yellow.

- How many primary colors is the girl sorting?

Name _____

Color and Shape

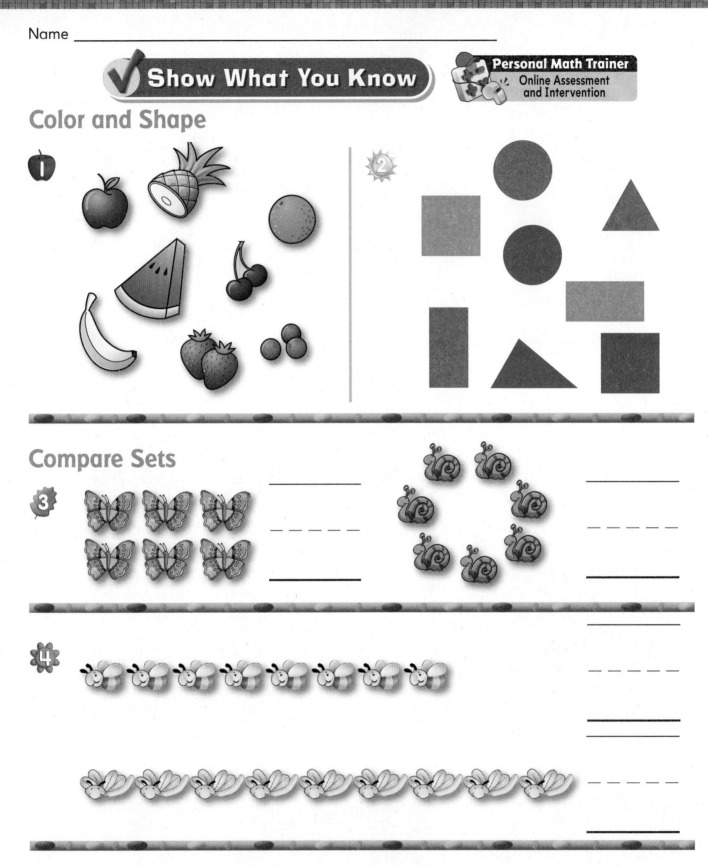

Compare Sets

This page checks understanding of important skills needed for success in Chapter 12.

DIRECTIONS 1. Circle the fruits that are red. 2. Circle the triangles. 3. Count and write how many in each set. Circle the set with more objects. 4. Count and write how many in each set. Circle the set with fewer objects.

Name _____

Vocabulary Builder

different

alike

DIRECTIONS Tell what you know about the ladybugs. Some of the ladybugs are different. Circle those ladybugs and tell why they are different. Tell what you know about the butterflies.

• Interactive Student Edition
• Multimedia eGlossary

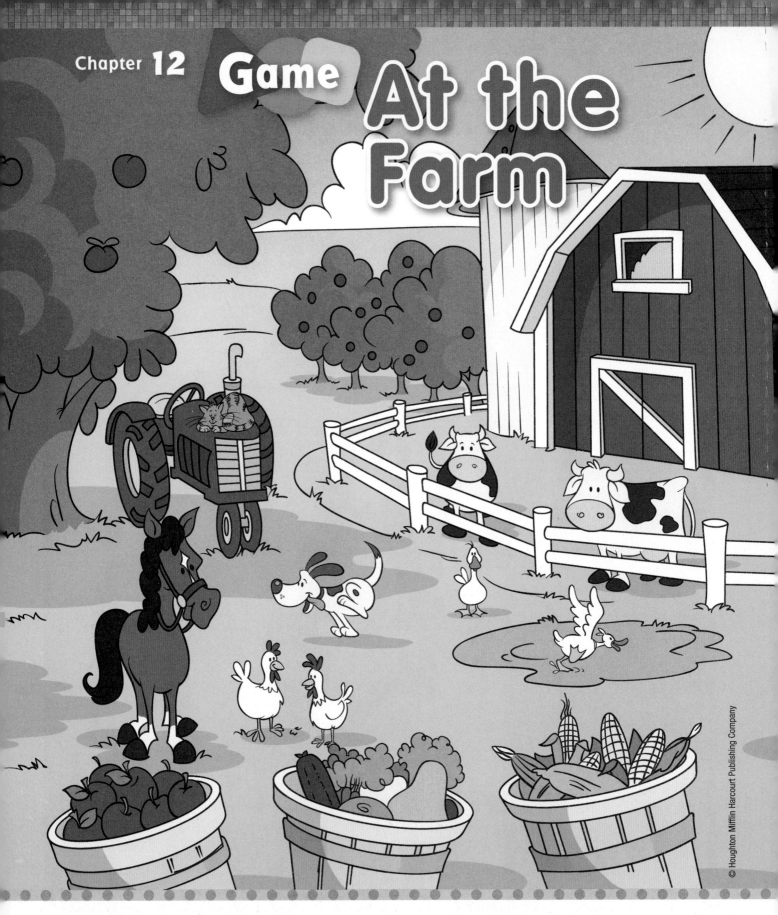

Chapter 12

Game

At the Farm

DIRECTIONS Use the picture to play with a partner. Decide who will go first. Player 1 looks at the picture, selects an object, and tells Player 2 the color of the object. Player 2 must guess what Player 1 sees. Once Player 2 guesses correctly, it is his or her turn to choose an object and have Player 1 guess.

Chapter 12 Vocabulary

big grande 8	**color (blue)** color (azul) 9
category categoría 10	**classify** clasificar 12
graph gráfica 30	**color (green)** color (verde) 32
color (red) color (rojo) 53	**shape** forma 61

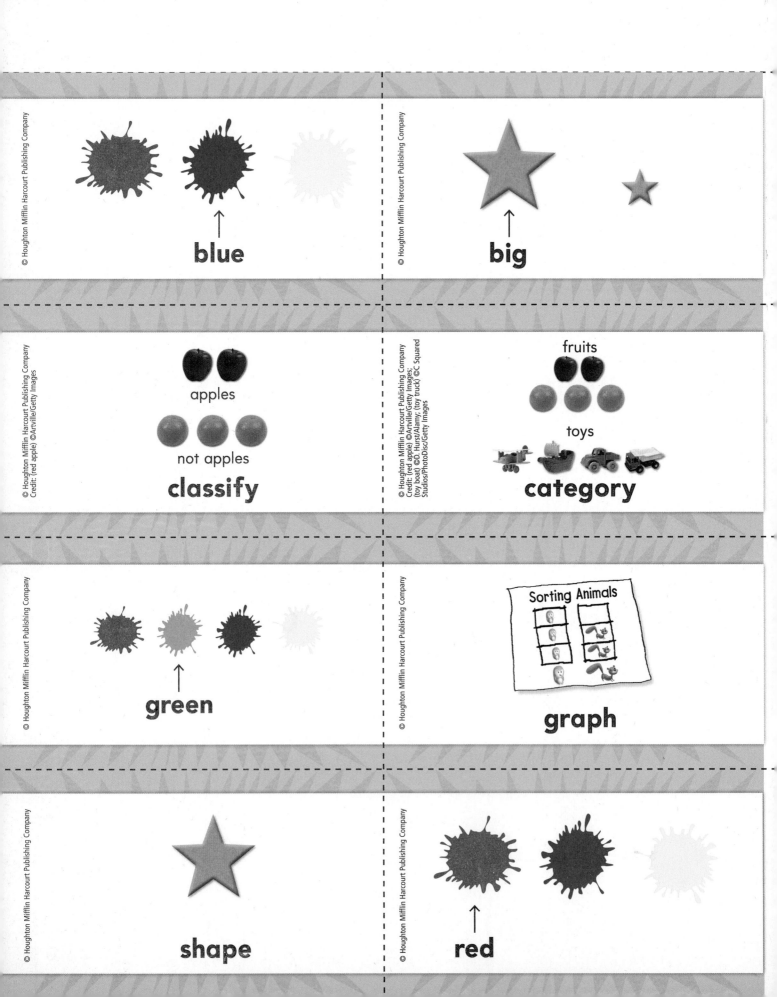

blue

big

apples

not apples

classify

fruits

toys

category

green

Sorting Animals

graph

shape

red

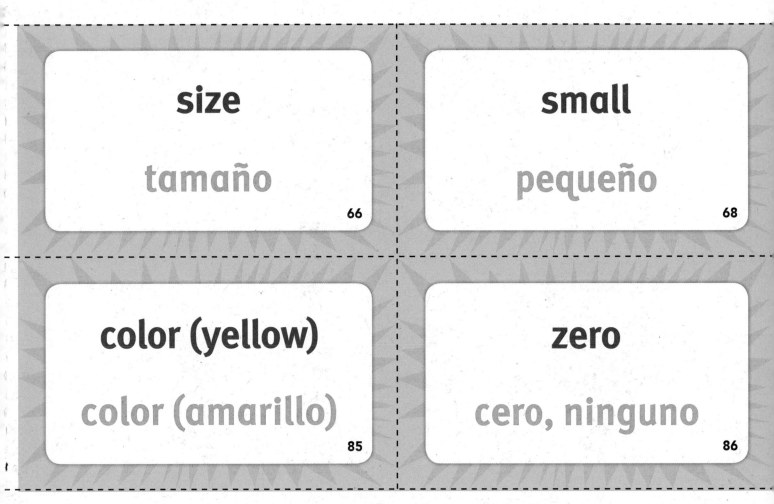

size

tamaño

66

small

pequeño

68

color (yellow)

color (amarillo)

85

zero

cero, ninguno

86

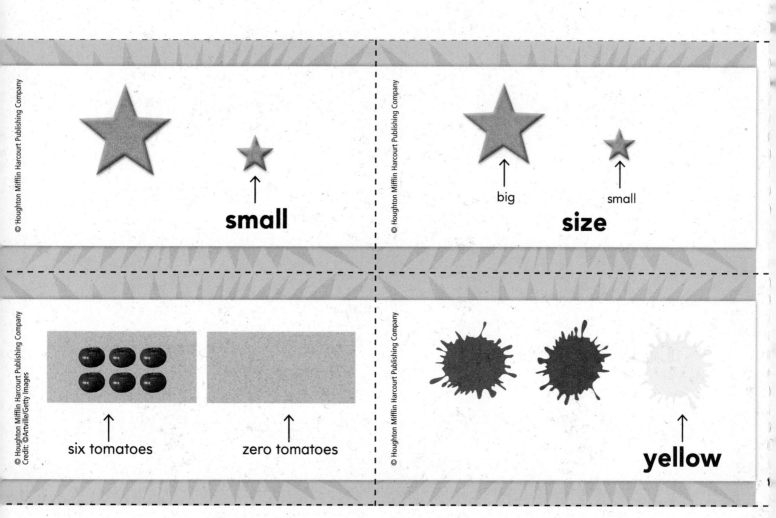

small

size

big small

six tomatoes

zero tomatoes

yellow

Game

Guess the Word

© Houghton Mifflin Harcourt Publishing Company • Image Credits: (bg) ©PhotoDisc/Getty Images; (t) ©Jamie Farrant/iStockphoto.com

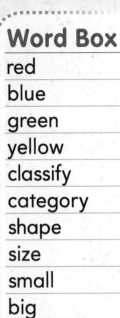

Word Box
red
blue
green
yellow
classify
category
shape
size
small
big
graph

Secret Words

Player 1					
Player 2					

DIRECTIONS Players take turns. A player chooses a secret word from the Word Box and then sets the timer. The player gives hints about the secret word. If the other player guesses the secret word before time runs out, he or she puts a connecting cube in the chart. The first player who has connecting cubes in all his or her boxes is the winner.

MATERIALS timer, connecting cubes for each player

The Write Way

DIRECTIONS Choose one idea. • Draw to show how to classify objects by size. • Draw to show a graph. **Reflect** Be ready to tell about your drawing.

Name _____

Algebra • Classify and Count by Color

Essential Question How can you classify and count objects by color?

Learning Objective You will sort, classify, and count objects by the attribute of color.

Listen and Draw

not

DIRECTIONS Choose a color. Use that color crayon to color the clouds. Sort and classify a handful of shapes into a set of that color and a set of not that color. Draw and color the shapes.

Chapter 12 • Lesson 1

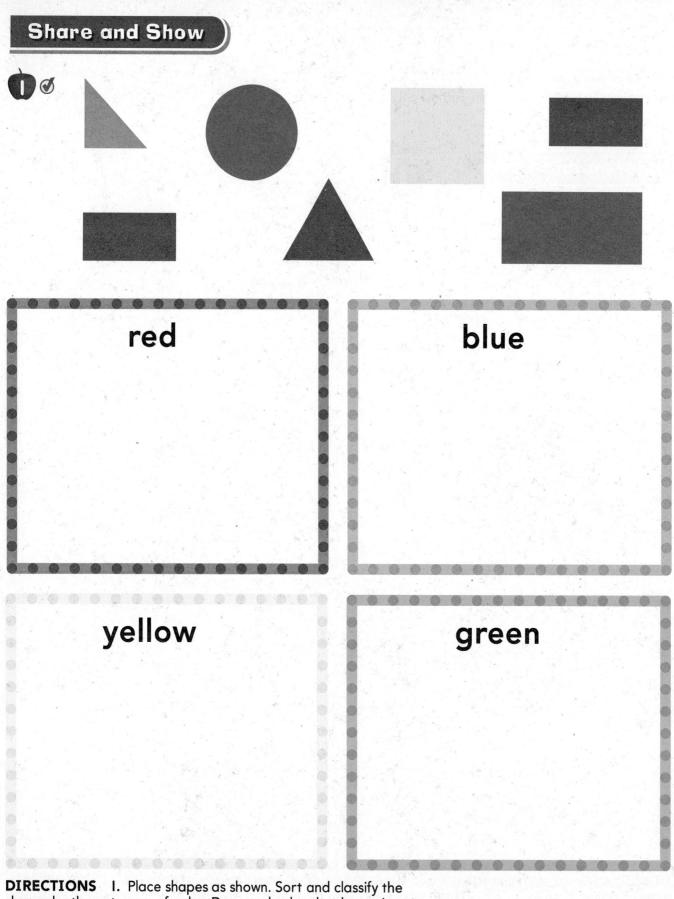

DIRECTIONS 1. Place shapes as shown. Sort and classify the shapes by the category of color. Draw and color the shapes in each category.

Name _____

☀ ②

1

red	blue
yellow	green

_____

- - - - - - -

_____

🍁 ③

2

red	blue
yellow	green

_____

- - - - - - -

_____

✿ ④

3

red	blue
yellow	green

_____

- - - - - - -

_____

DIRECTIONS Look at the categories of color in Exercise 1. Count how many in each category. **2.** Circle the categories of color that have one shape. Write the number. **3.** Circle the category that has two shapes. Write the number. **4.** Circle the category that has three shapes. Write the number.

Problem Solving • Applications

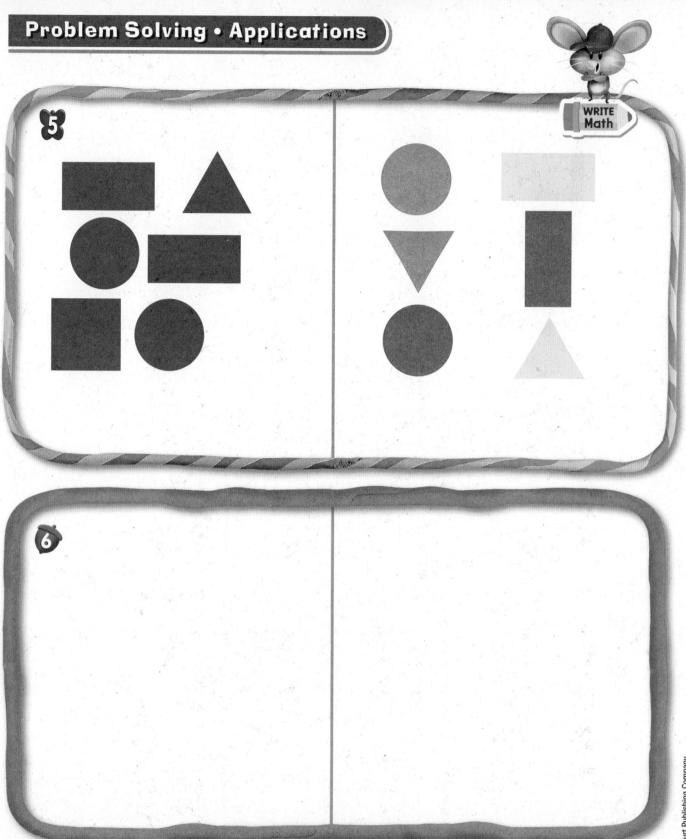

DIRECTIONS 5. Ava placed her shapes as shown. How did she sort and classify her shapes? Draw one more shape in each category. 6. Draw to show what you know about sorting and classifying by color.

HOME ACTIVITY • Provide your child with different colors of the same objects, such as straws, socks, or toys. Ask him or her to sort and classify the objects into two sets, a set of all one color and a set of all the other colors.

Algebra • Classify and Count by Color

Learning Objective You will sort, classify, and count objects by the attribute of color.

1

yellow	red

2

3 | yellow | red | _____

_____

DIRECTIONS **1.** Place a yellow square, red triangle, red rectangle, yellow square, and red triangle at the top of the page as shown. Sort and classify the shapes by the category of color. Draw and color the shapes in each category. **2.** Look at the categories in Exercise 1. Count how many in each category. Circle the category that has 3 shapes. Write the number.

Lesson Check

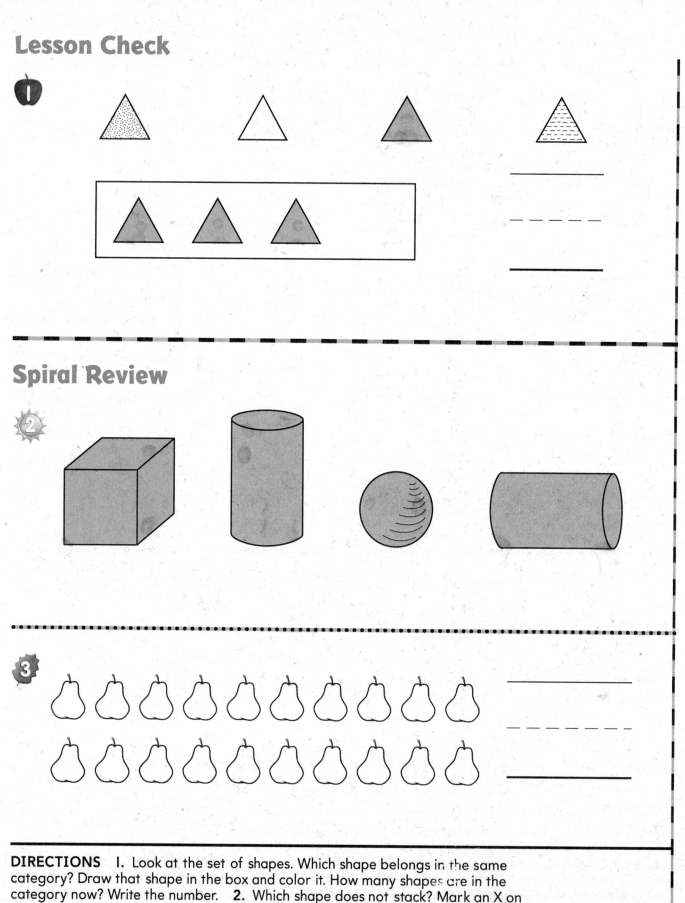

1

Spiral Review

2

3

DIRECTIONS **1.** Look at the set of shapes. Which shape belongs in the same category? Draw that shape in the box and color it. How many shapes are in the category now? Write the number. **2.** Which shape does not stack? Mark an X on the shape. **3.** Count and tell how many pieces of fruit. Write the number.

692 six hundred ninety-two

FOR MORE PRACTICE
GO TO THE
Personal Math Trainer

Name _____

Algebra • Classify and Count by Shape

Essential Question How can you classify and count objects by shape?

Learning Objective You will sort, classify, and count objects by the attribute of shape.

Listen and Draw

not

DIRECTIONS Choose a shape. Draw the shape at the top of each side. Sort and classify a handful of shapes into a set of the shape you chose and a set that is not that shape. Draw and color the shapes.

Chapter 12 • Lesson 2

© Houghton Mifflin Harcourt Publishing Company

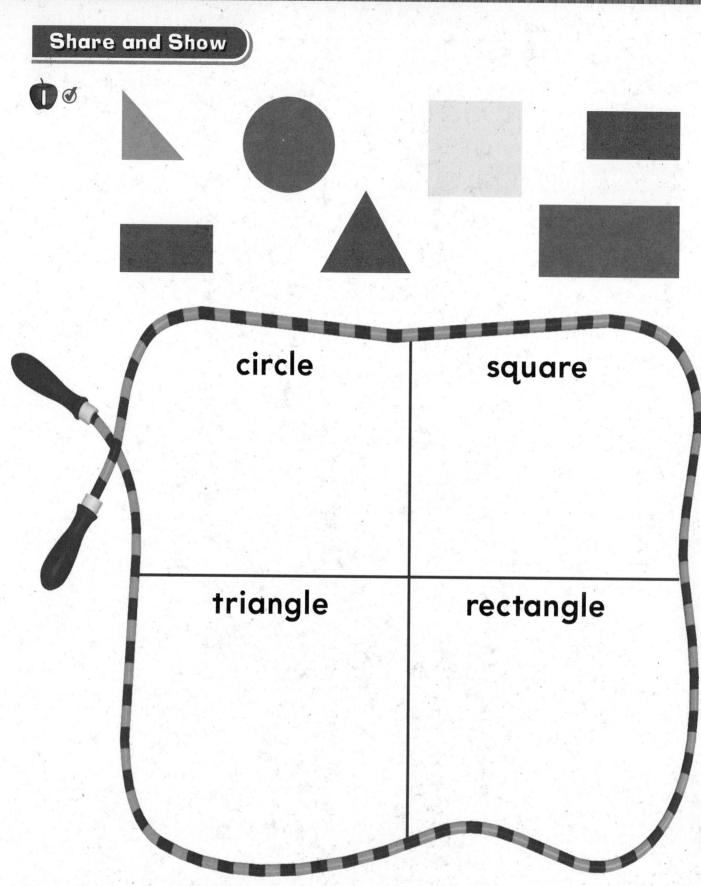

circle

square

triangle

rectangle

DIRECTIONS 1. Place shapes as shown. Sort and classify the shapes by the category of shape. Draw and color the shapes in each category.

Name _____

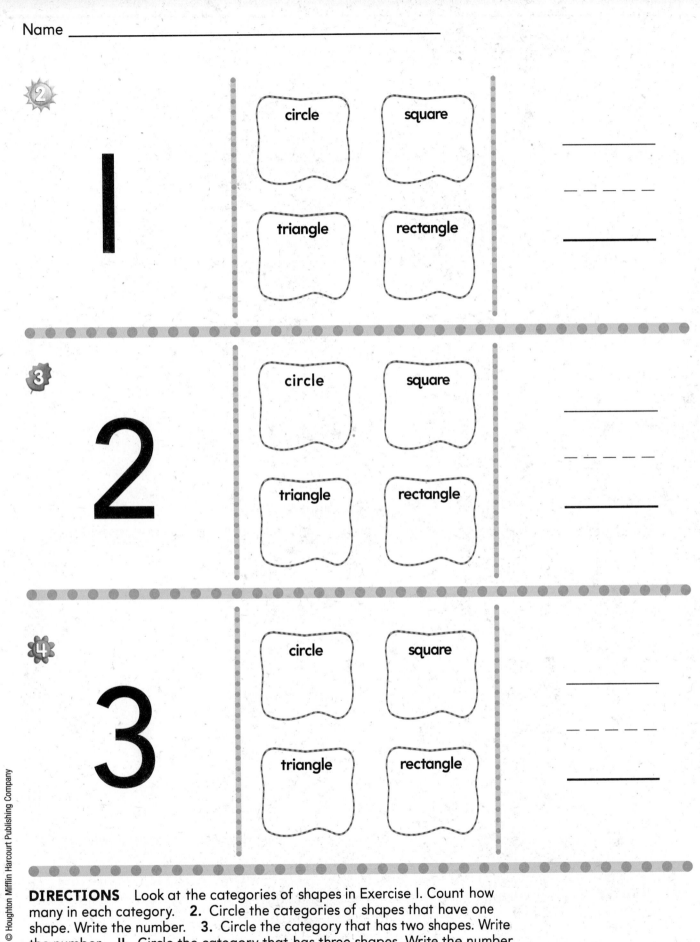

② 1

| circle | square |
| triangle | rectangle |

_____
- - - - - - -
_____

③ 2

| circle | square |
| triangle | rectangle |

_____
- - - - - - -
_____

④ 3

| circle | square |
| triangle | rectangle |

_____
- - - - - - -
_____

DIRECTIONS Look at the categories of shapes in Exercise 1. Count how many in each category. **2.** Circle the categories of shapes that have one shape. Write the number. **3.** Circle the category that has two shapes. Write the number. **4.** Circle the category that has three shapes. Write the number.

Problem Solving • Applications

WRITE
Math

5

6

DIRECTIONS **5.** Brandon used his shapes. How did he sort and classify his shapes? Draw one more shape in each category. **6.** Using the same shapes, draw to show what you know about sorting and classifying by shape in a different way.

HOME ACTIVITY • Have your child sort objects in a house into categories of shape.

696 six hundred ninety-six

Name _____

Algebra • Classify and Count by Shape

Learning Objective You will sort, classify, and count objects by the attribute of shape.

1

triangle	circle

2

2 | triangle | circle | _____

DIRECTIONS **1.** Place a green triangle, blue circle, red triangle, and blue circle at the top of the page as shown. Sort and classify the shapes by the category of shape. Draw and color the shapes in each category. **2.** Look at the categories in Exercise 1. Count how many in each category. Circle the categories that have two shapes. Write the number.

Chapter 12

six hundred ninety-seven **697**

Lesson Check

1.

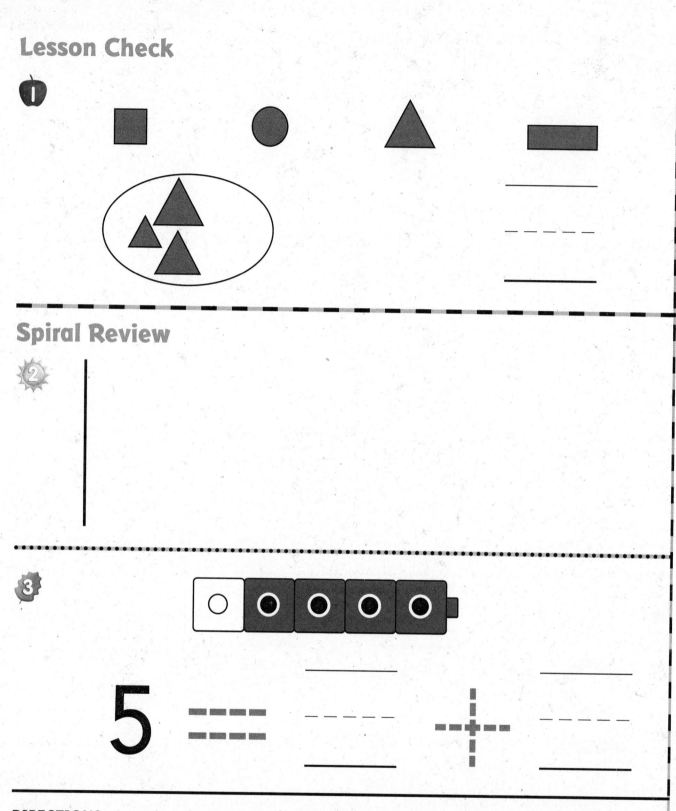

Spiral Review

2.

3.

5 $=$ ___ _ _ _ $+$ _ _ _

___

DIRECTIONS **1.** Look at the set of shapes. Which shape belongs in the same category? Draw that shape in the oval. How many shapes are in the category now? Write the number. **2.** Find two crayons. Place one end of each crayon on the line. Compare the lengths. Draw the crayons. Say *longer than*, *shorter than*, or *about the same length* to describe the lengths. Circle both crayons if they are about the same length. Circle the longer crayon if one crayon is longer than the other. **3.** Complete the addition sentence to show the numbers that match the cube train.

698 six hundred ninety-eight

FOR MORE PRACTICE
GO TO THE
Personal Math Trainer

Name _____

Algebra • Classify and Count by Size

Essential Question How can you classify and count objects by size?

Learning Objective You will sort, classify, and count objects by the attribute of size.

Listen and Draw

big	small

DIRECTIONS Sort and classify a handful of shapes by size. Draw and color the shapes.

© Houghton Mifflin Harcourt Publishing Company

Share and Show

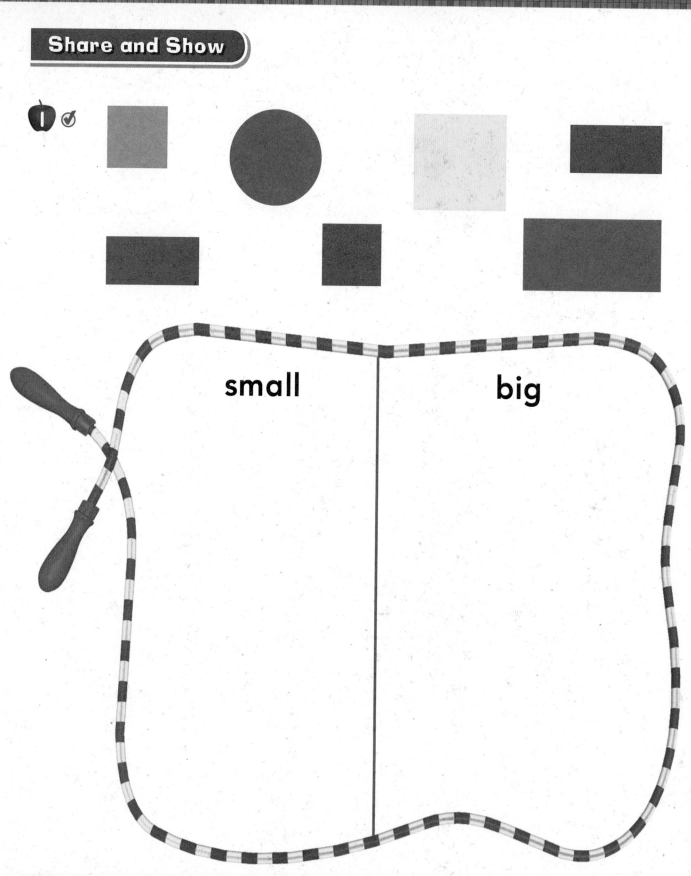

1 ✓

small   big

DIRECTIONS **1.** Place shapes as shown. Sort and classify the shapes by the category of size. Draw and color the shapes in each category.

700 seven hundred

② 4

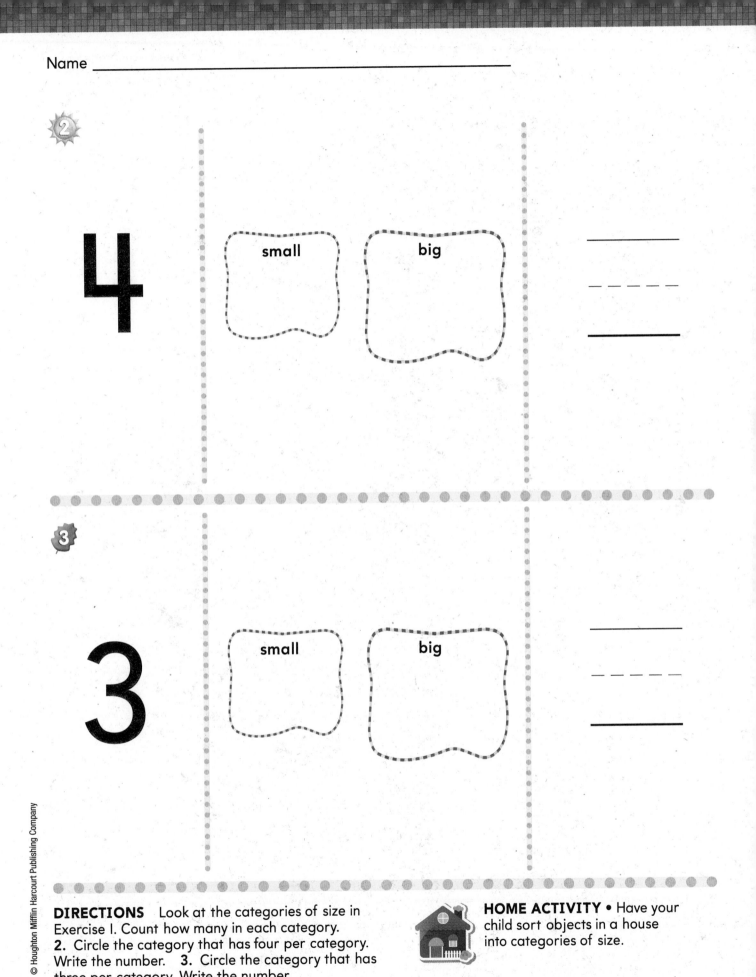

| small | big |

_____
- - - - -
_____

③ 3

| small | big |

_____
- - - - -
_____

DIRECTIONS Look at the categories of size in Exercise 1. Count how many in each category. **2.** Circle the category that has four per category. Write the number. **3.** Circle the category that has three per category. Write the number.

HOME ACTIVITY • Have your child sort objects in a house into categories of size.

✓ **Mid-Chapter Checkpoint**

Personal Math Trainer
Online Assessment
and Intervention

Concepts and Skills

1

2

3 THINK SMARTER

Big	Small		Big	Small		Big	Small

DIRECTIONS 1. Look at the set at the beginning of the row. Circle the shape that belongs in that set. 2. Look at the shape at the beginning of the row. Mark an X on the set in which the shape belongs. 3. Mark under the chart that shows the shapes correctly classified.

702 seven hundred two

© Houghton Mifflin Harcourt Publishing Company

Algebra • Classify and Count by Size

Learning Objective You will sort, classify, and count objects by the attribute of size.

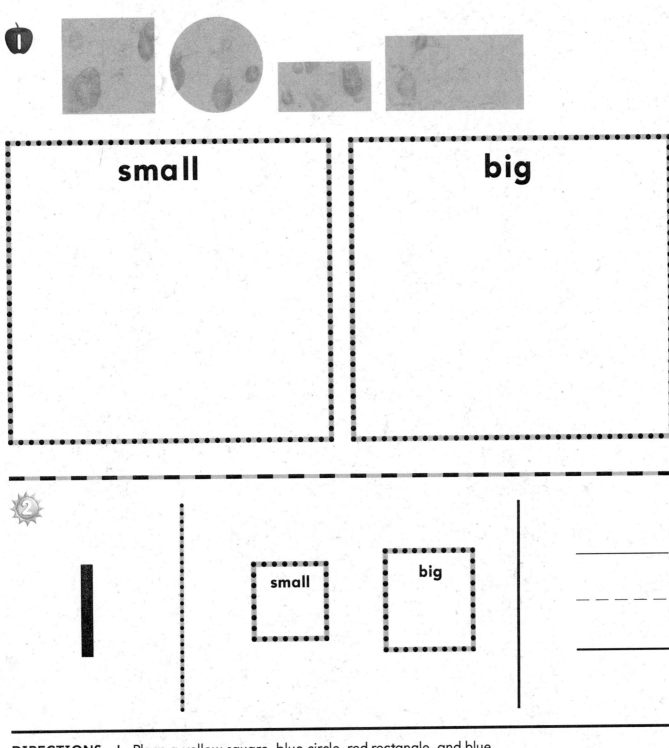

small

big

② small   big   _____
              _ _ _ _ _
              _____

DIRECTIONS 1. Place a yellow square, blue circle, red rectangle, and blue rectangle at the top of the page as shown. Sort and classify the shapes by the category of size. Draw and color the shapes in each category. 2. Look at the categories in Exercise 1. Count how many in each category. Circle the category that has one per category. Write the number.

Lesson Check

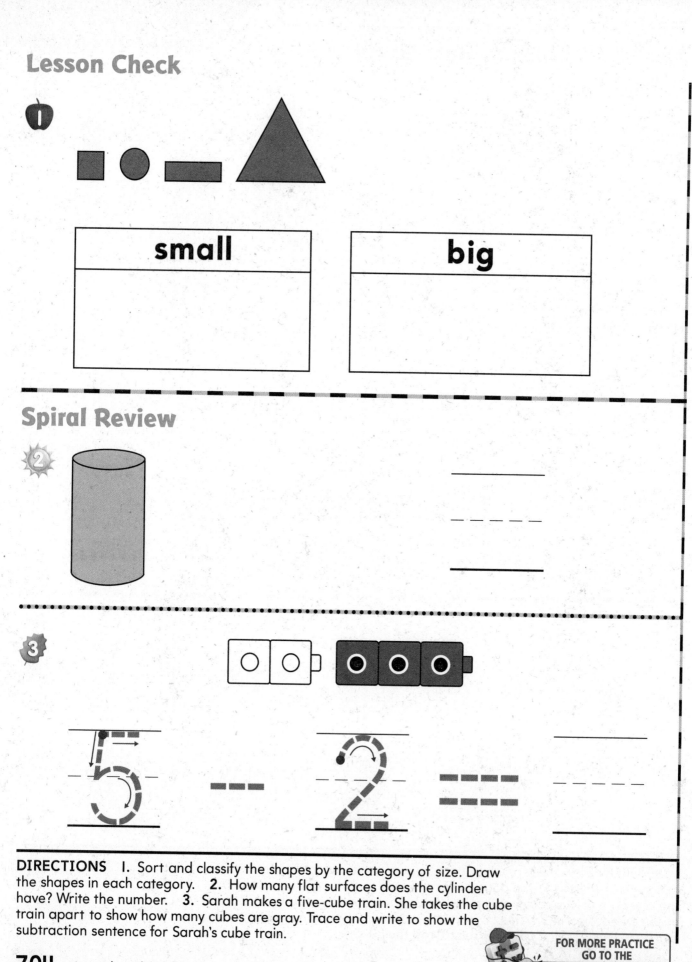

①

small	big

Spiral Review

②

③

$$5 - 2$$

DIRECTIONS 1. Sort and classify the shapes by the category of size. Draw the shapes in each category. 2. How many flat surfaces does the cylinder have? Write the number. 3. Sarah makes a five-cube train. She takes the cube train apart to show how many cubes are gray. Trace and write to show the subtraction sentence for Sarah's cube train.

FOR MORE PRACTICE GO TO THE Personal Math Trainer

Name _____

Make a Concrete Graph

Essential Question How can you make a graph to count objects that have been classified into categories?

Learning Objective You will make a graph to count objects that have been classified into categories.

Listen and Draw

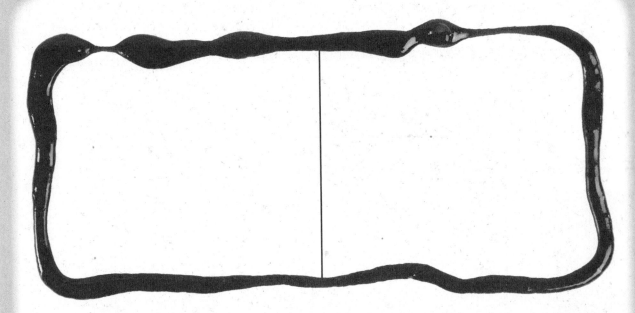

Orange and Green Cubes

DIRECTIONS Place a handful of orange and green cubes on the workspace. Sort and classify the cubes by the category of color. Move the cubes to the graph by category. Draw and color the cubes. Tell a friend how many in each category.

© Houghton Mifflin Harcourt Publishing Company

Chapter 12 • Lesson 4

seven hundred five **705**

Share and Show

1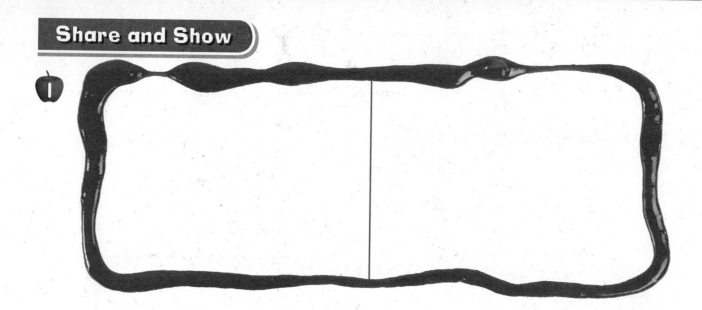

2 ✓

Red and Blue Cubes				

3 ✓

_____
- - - - - - -
_____

_____
- - - - - - -
_____

DIRECTIONS 1. Place a handful of red and blue cubes on the workspace. Sort and classify the cubes by category. 2. Move the cubes to the graph. Draw and color the cubes. 3. Write how many of each cube.

Name _____

4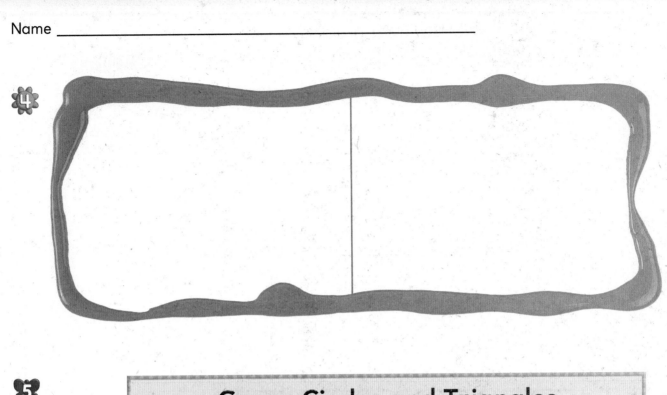

5

Green Circles and Triangles					

6

_____   _____
- - - - -   - - - - -
_____

DIRECTIONS **4.** Place a handful of green circles and triangles on the workspace. Sort and classify the shapes by category. **5.** Move the shapes to the graph. Draw and color the shapes. **6.** Write how many of each shape.

Problem Solving • Applications Real World

WRITE
Math

7

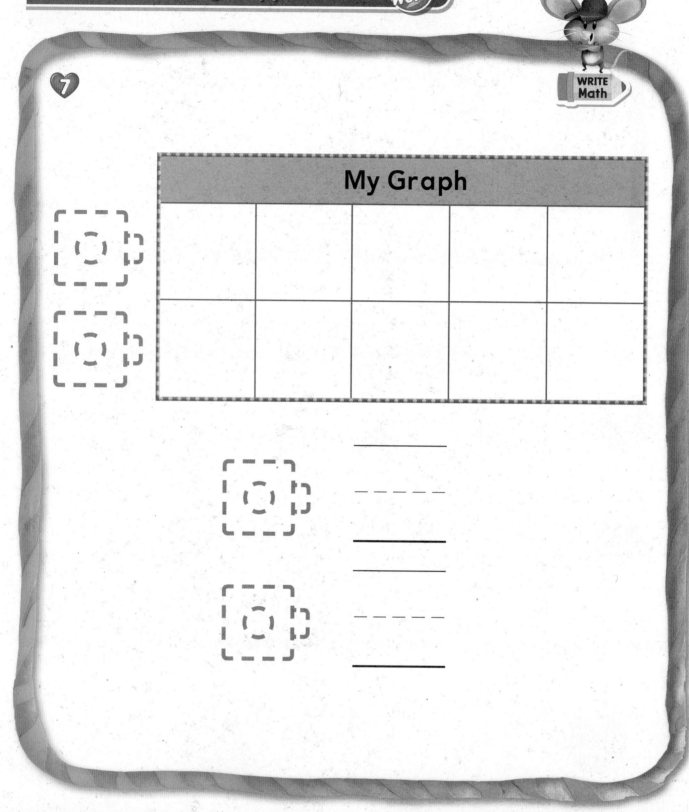

My Graph

© Houghton Mifflin Harcourt Publishing Company

DIRECTIONS **7.** Use five cubes of two colors. Color the cubes to show the categories. Draw and color to show what you know about making a graph with those cubes. How many are in each category? Write the numbers.

HOME ACTIVITY • Have your child tell about the graph that he or she made on this page.

Name _____

Make a Concrete Graph

Learning Objective You will make a graph to count objects that have been classified into categories.

1

2

Circles and Triangles					

3

_____

- - - - - - -

_____   _____

- - - - - - -

_____

DIRECTIONS 1. Place a handful of green circles and triangles on the workspace. Sort and classify the shapes by category. **2.** Move the shapes to the graph. Draw and color the shapes. **3.** Write how many of each shape.

Lesson Check

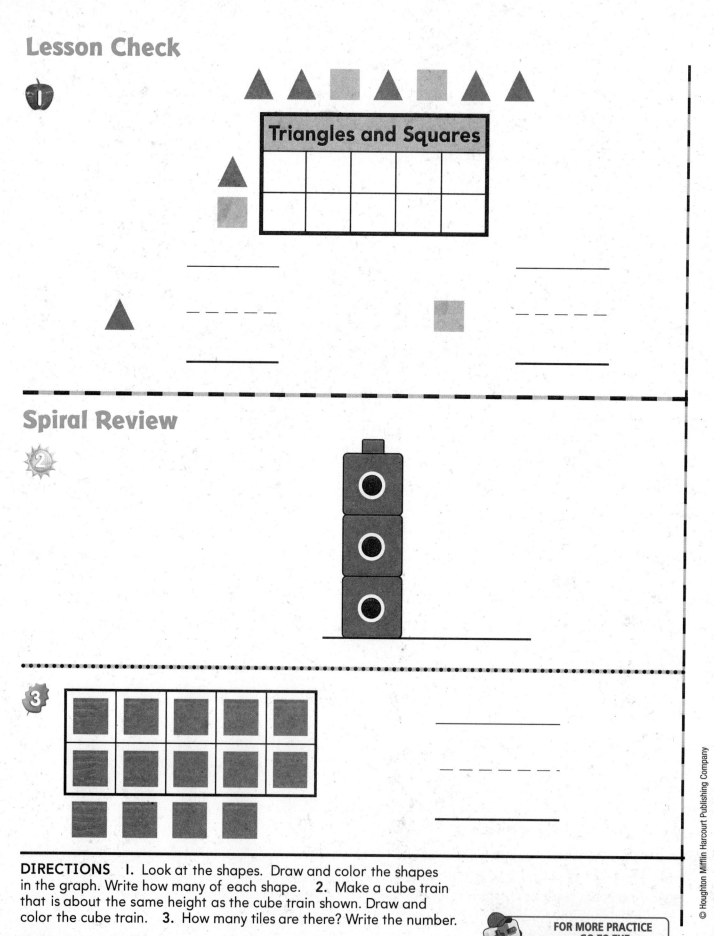

Triangles and Squares

Spiral Review

DIRECTIONS 1. Look at the shapes. Draw and color the shapes in the graph. Write how many of each shape. 2. Make a cube train that is about the same height as the cube train shown. Draw and color the cube train. 3. How many tiles are there? Write the number.

FOR MORE PRACTICE GO TO THE Personal Math Trainer

Name _____

Problem Solving • Read a Graph

Essential Question How can you read a graph to count objects that have been classified into categories?

Learning Objective You will read a graph and count objects that have been classified into categories to solve problems.

🔑 Unlock the Problem

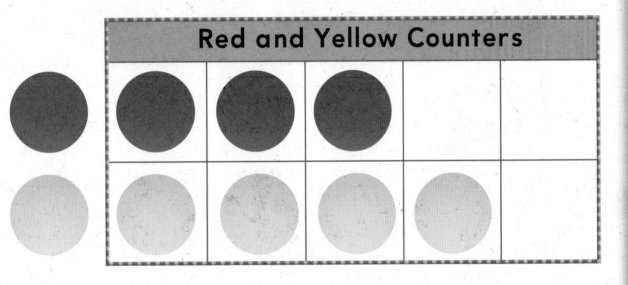

Red and Yellow Counters

DIRECTIONS Erin made a graph of her counters. How many counters are in each category? Trace the numbers. Trace the circle to show which category has more counters.

Chapter 12 • Lesson 5

seven hundred eleven **711**

© Houghton Mifflin Harcourt Publishing Company

Counter Colors

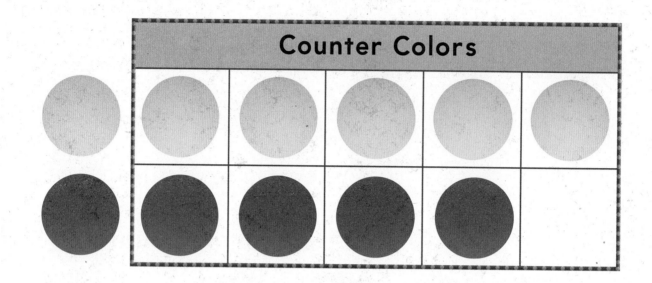

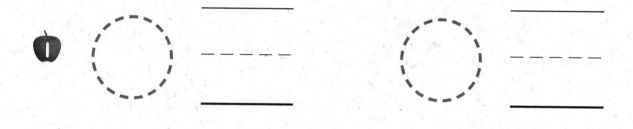

1

2

DIRECTIONS 1. Billy made a graph showing his counters. Color the counters to show his categories. How many counters are in each category? Write the numbers. **2.** Circle the category that has more counters on the graph.

Name _____

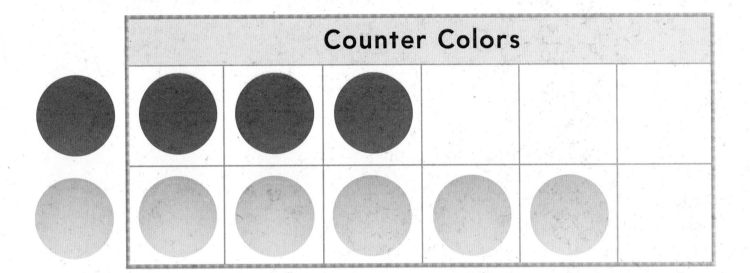

Counter Colors

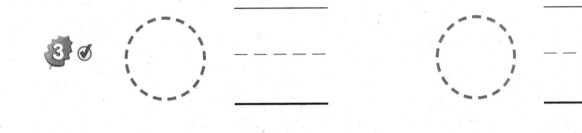

③ ✓

④ ✓

DIRECTIONS 3. Rong made a graph of her counters. Color the counters to show her categories. How many counters are in each category? Write the numbers.
4. Circle the category that has fewer counters on the graph.

On Your Own (Real World)

WRITE
Math

5

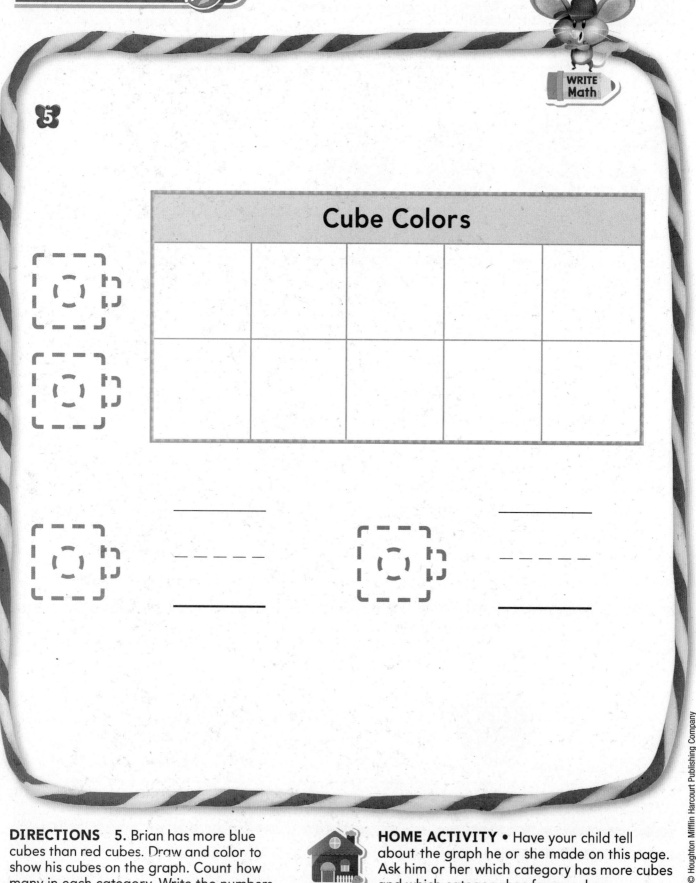

Cube Colors

DIRECTIONS 5. Brian has more blue cubes than red cubes. Draw and color to show his cubes on the graph. Count how many in each category. Write the numbers.

 HOME ACTIVITY • Have your child tell about the graph he or she made on this page. Ask him or her which category has more cubes and which category has fewer cubes.

Name _____

Read a Graph

Learning Objective You will read a graph and count objects that have been classified into categories to solve problems.

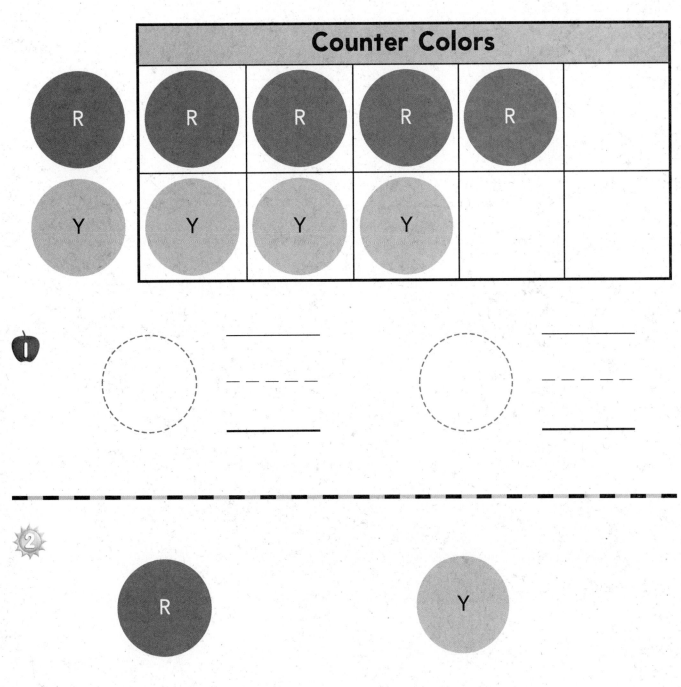

DIRECTIONS 1. Color the counters to show the categories. R is for red, and Y is for yellow. How many counters are in each category? Write the numbers. 2. Circle the category that has more counters on the graph.

Chapter 12

Lesson Check

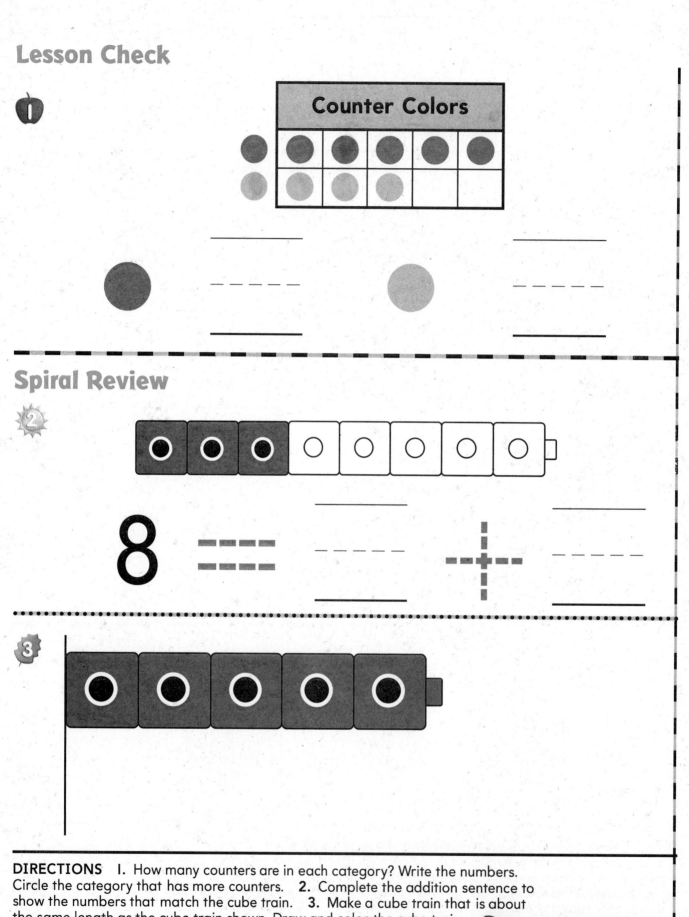

Counter Colors

Spiral Review

8 = ___ + ___

DIRECTIONS 1. How many counters are in each category? Write the numbers. Circle the category that has more counters. 2. Complete the addition sentence to show the numbers that match the cube train. 3. Make a cube train that is about the same length as the cube train shown. Draw and color the cube train.

FOR MORE PRACTICE GO TO THE Personal Math Trainer

Name _____

Personal Math Trainer
Online Assessment
and Intervention

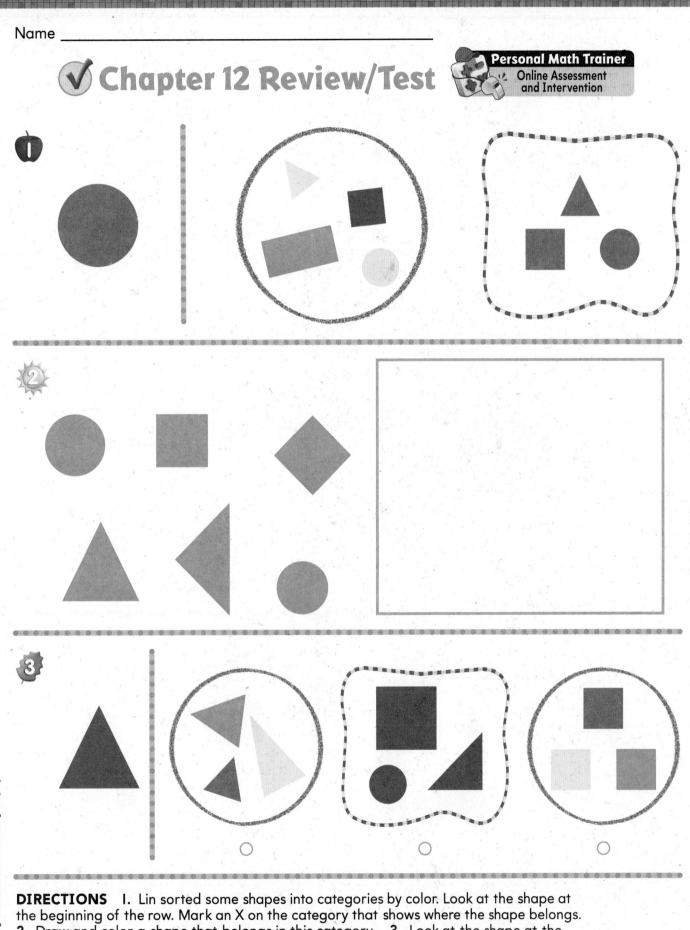

DIRECTIONS **1.** Lin sorted some shapes into categories by color. Look at the shape at the beginning of the row. Mark an X on the category that shows where the shape belongs.
2. Draw and color a shape that belongs in this category. **3.** Look at the shape at the beginning of the row. Mark under all of the categories the shape can belong.

© Houghton Mifflin Harcourt Publishing Company

Chapter 12

Assessment Options
Chapter Test

seven hundred seventeen **717**

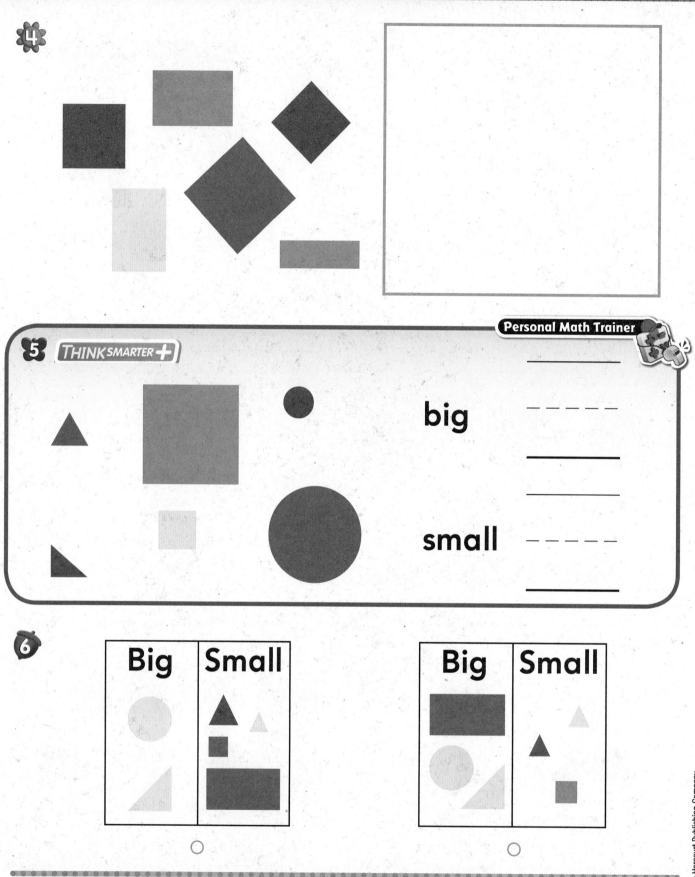

4

5 THINK SMARTER +

Personal Math Trainer

big

small

6

Big	Small

Big	Small

○   ○

DIRECTIONS 4. Draw and color a shape that belongs in this category.
5. Mark an X on each big shape. Write how many big objects. Draw a circle around each of the small objects. Write how many small objects. **6.** Mark under the chart that shows the shapes correctly classified.

718 seven hundred eighteen

Name _____

7 THINK SMARTER ＋

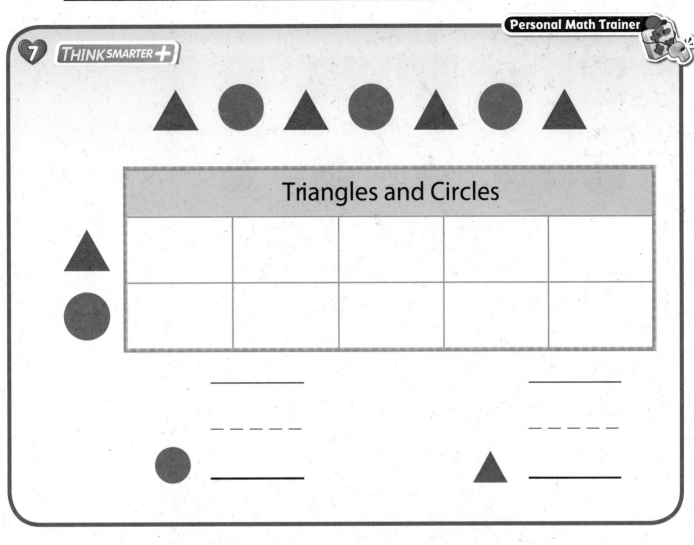

Triangles and Circles

▲				
●				

_____   _____

_ _ _ _ _   _ _ _ _ _

● _____   ▲ _____

8

Blue Squares and Circles

●	●	●	●	
■	■	■		

DIRECTIONS **7.** Sort and classify the shapes by category. Draw each shape on the graph. Write how many of each shape. **8.** Jake sorted some shapes. Then he made a graph. Count how many shapes there are in each category. Mark an X on the category that has more shapes.

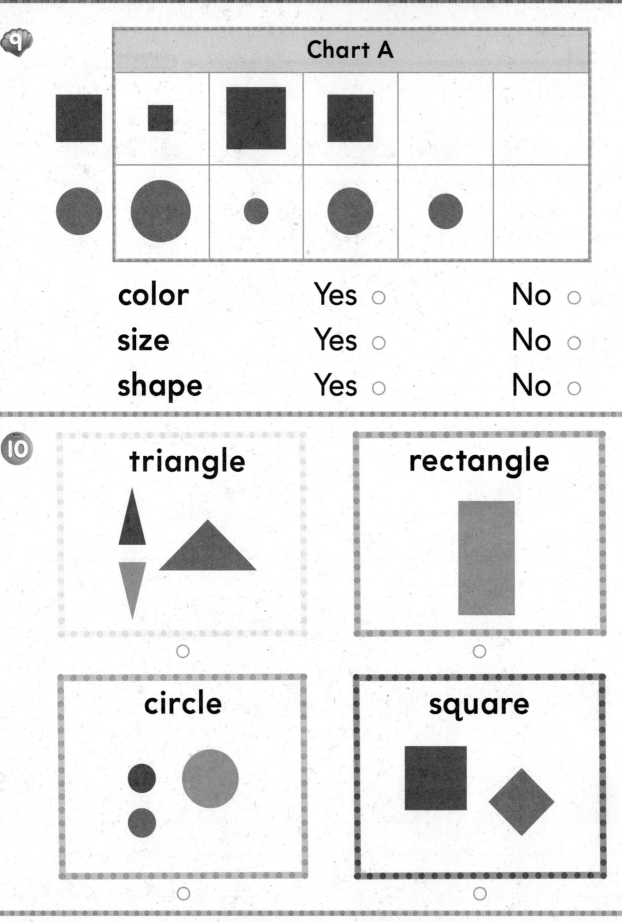

Chart A

■	▪	■	■	
●	●	●	●	●

color   Yes ○   No ○

size   Yes ○   No ○

shape   Yes ○   No ○

triangle ○

rectangle ○

circle ○

square ○

DIRECTIONS **9.** Is this chart sorted by color, size, and shape? Choose Yes or No. **10.** Choose all of the sets with the same number of objects.

720 seven hundred twenty

Name _____

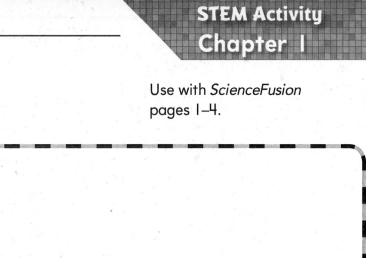
Our Senses
Develop Concepts

Use with *ScienceFusion*
pages 1–4.

1

2

3

4

© Houghton Mifflin Harcourt Publishing Company

DIRECTIONS 1. Draw one object you can hear. 2. Draw two objects you can smell. 3. Draw three objects you can see. 4. Draw four objects you can taste.

Sum It Up!

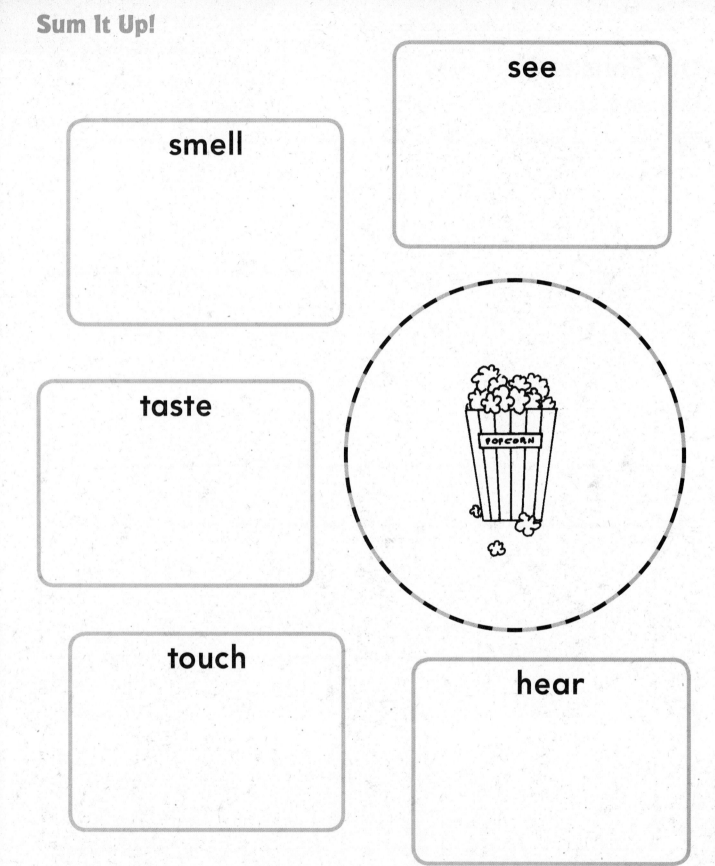

see

smell

taste

touch

hear

POPCORN

DIRECTIONS Draw to show what you know about your senses using popcorn.

STEM 2

Name _____

Recycling Paper
Develop Concepts

Use with *ScienceFusion*
pages 103–104.

DIRECTIONS   Draw a line from the object to its container.

Sum It Up!

DIRECTIONS Count the metal cans, the objects made of paper, and the plastic bottles. Write how many of each object. Circle the number that is the greatest.

STEM 4

Name _____

Rocks
Develop Concepts

Use with *ScienceFusion*
pages 63–66.

1 _____

_ _ _ _ _ _ _ _ _

_____ rocks

2 _____

_ _ _ _ _ _ _

I found _____ rocks.

DIRECTIONS **1.** These rocks have different sizes, shapes, and textures.
Count the rocks. Write how many. **2.** Find some rocks. Write how many
rocks you found.

Sum It Up!

3 _____

_ _ _ _ _ _ _ _

_____ rocks in the sandbox

4 _____

_ _ _ _ _ _ _ _

_____ rocks outside the sandbox

5 _____

_ _ _ _ _ _ _ _

_____ rocks in all

DIRECTIONS 3. Count the rocks in the sandbox. Write how many. 4. Count the rocks outside the sandbox. Write how many. 5. Count all the rocks in the picture. Write how many.

STEM 6

Name _____

Living and Nonliving
Develop Concepts

Use with *ScienceFusion*
pages 105–108.

1

2

3

DIRECTIONS 1. Draw a picture of a living thing. 2. Draw a picture
of a nonliving thing. 3. Draw a picture of a basic need of a living thing.

Sum It Up!

_____

- - - - - - - - -   living things

_____

_____

- - - - - - - - -   nonliving things

_____

DIRECTIONS Circle each living thing. Mark an X on each nonliving thing. Write how many living things. Write how many nonliving things.

STEM 8

Name _____

Aquarium Design
Design It: Model Terrarium

Use with *ScienceFusion* pages 137–138.

$$5 + 3 = 8$$

DIRECTIONS Use two colors to color objects in the terrarium that models the addition sentence.

Develop Concepts

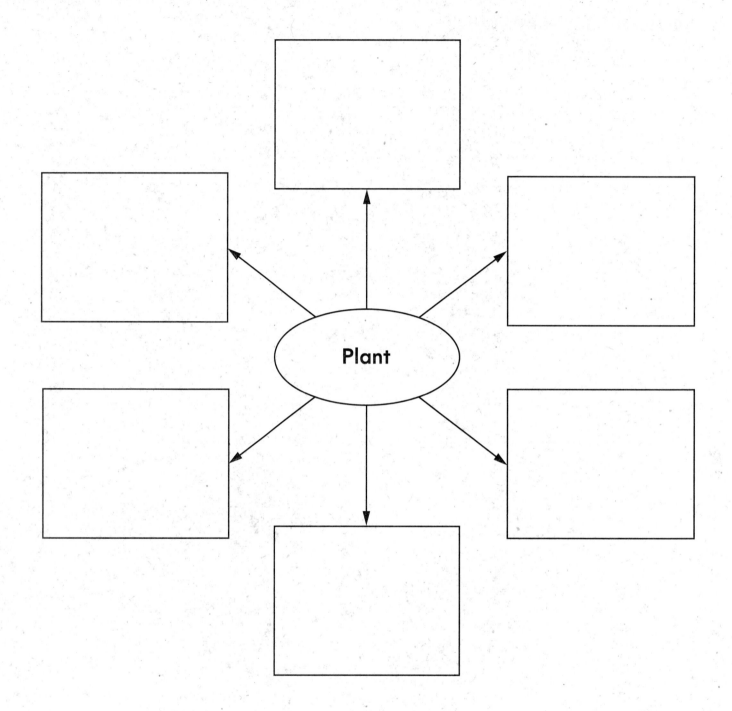

Plant

DIRECTIONS Describe the basic needs of a terrarium.

Name ______________________________

Many Animals

Develop Concepts

Use with *ScienceFusion* pages 109–112.

Animals with Different Coverings

1

feathers		______

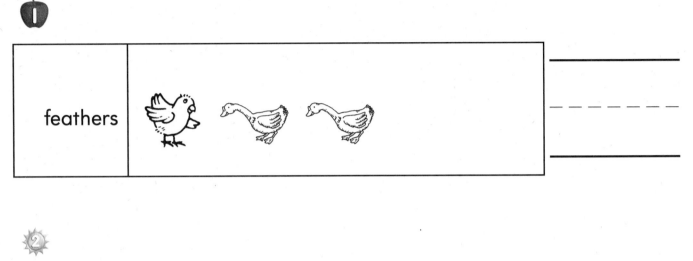

2

scales		______

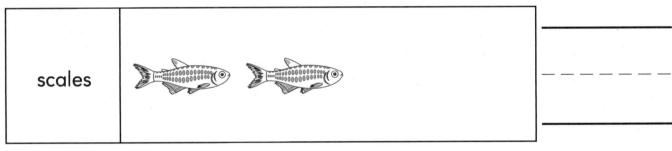

3

fur		______

DIRECTIONS 1–3. Count how many. Write the number.

Sum It Up!

❀ 4

_____

- - - - - - - - - animals with fur

_____

❀ 5

_____

- - - - - - - - - animals with feathers

_____

🌰 6

6 — 3 = _ _ _

DIRECTIONS 4. Count the animals with fur. Write the number. 5. Count the animals with feathers. Write the number. 6. Complete the subtraction sentence that shows the difference between the two numbers.

STEM 12

Plants Grow and Change
Develop Concepts

Use with *ScienceFusion*
pages 133–136.

DIRECTIONS   1. Draw to show what this seedling might grow into.

Sum It Up!

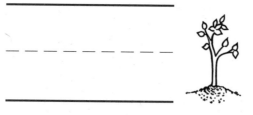

_____
- - - - - - - - - - - - - - - - - - - -
_____

DIRECTIONS **2.** Count the seedlings. Write the number.

STEM 14

Name _____

Night Sky
Develop Concepts

Use with *ScienceFusion* pages 99–102.

day   night

DIRECTIONS Circle the word that tells when we see stars in the sky.

Sum It Up!

_____

- - - - - - - - -

_____ stars

DIRECTIONS James counted stars in the sky. Circle sets of ten stars. Count the sets of stars by tens. Write how many.

STEM 16

Name _____

Matter
Develop Concepts

Use with *ScienceFusion*
pages 23–26.

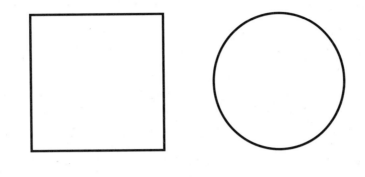

1

2

DIRECTIONS **1.** Draw an object that is shaped like a square. **2.** Draw an
object that is shaped like a circle.

Develop Concepts

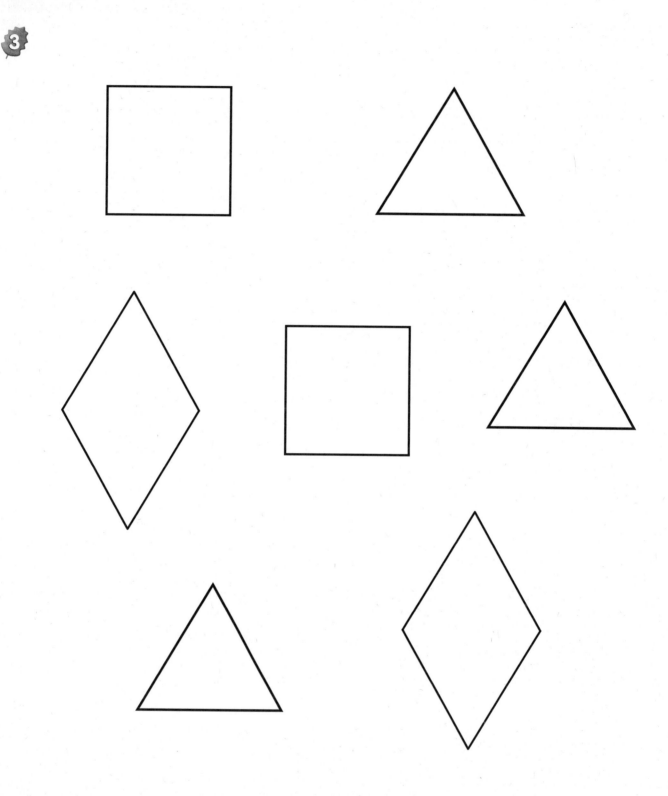

DIRECTIONS   **3.** Find which shapes are the same. Color all the shapes that are the same one color. Use as many colors as the types of shapes.

STEM 18

Name _____

Solving Problems
Develop Concepts

Use with *ScienceFusion*
pages 13–16.

1

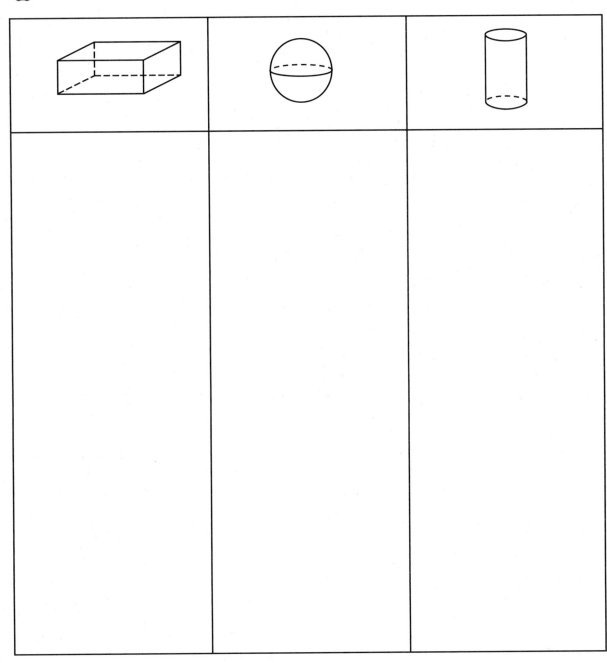

DIRECTIONS **1.** Find objects that are shaped like the shapes in the chart. In each column, draw to show the things you found.

Sum It Up!

2

	Does it roll?	Does it stack?	Does it slide?

3

DIRECTIONS **2.** Look at the shape at the beginning of each row. Decide if it can roll, stack, or slide. Mark an X or insert a check mark in each space to tell if that shape can roll, stack, or slide. **3.** Draw to show an object that rolls and does not stack.

STEM 20

Name _____

Light
Develop Concepts

Use with *ScienceFusion*
pages 33–36.

❶

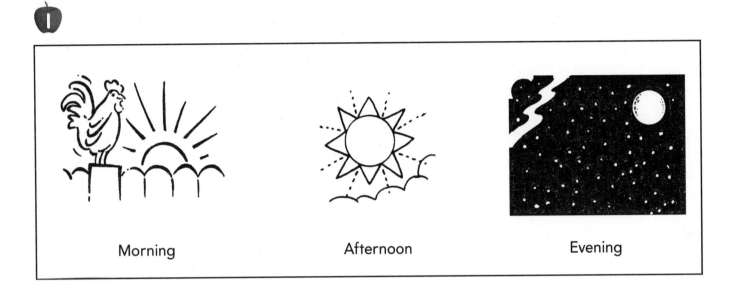

Morning   Afternoon   Evening

②

DIRECTIONS **1.** Look at the pictures. Circle one time of day.
2. Draw to show something you do at that time of the day.

Sum It Up!

Morning

Afternoon

Evening

DIRECTIONS **3.** Draw a line from the time of day to the shadow it may cause on the tree.

STEM 22

Name _____

Using Magnets
Develop Concepts

Use with *ScienceFusion*
pages 61–62.

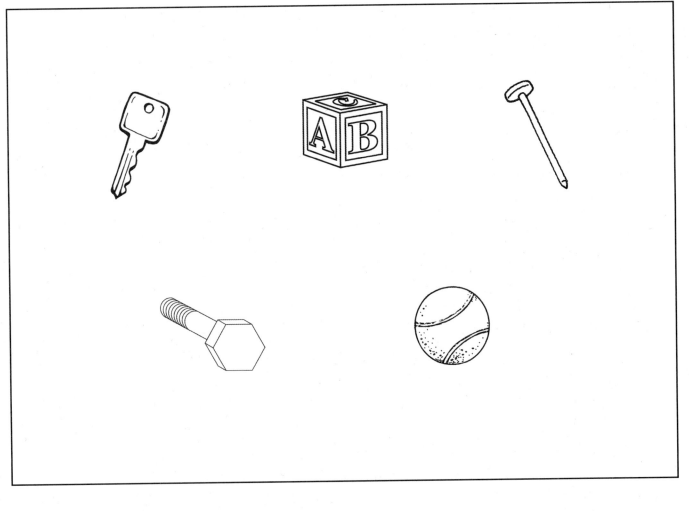

DIRECTIONS   **I.** Decide which objects the magnet will attract. Circle the objects the magnet will attract. Mark an X on objects the magnet will not attract.

Chapter 12 • STEM Activity   STEM 23

Sum It Up!

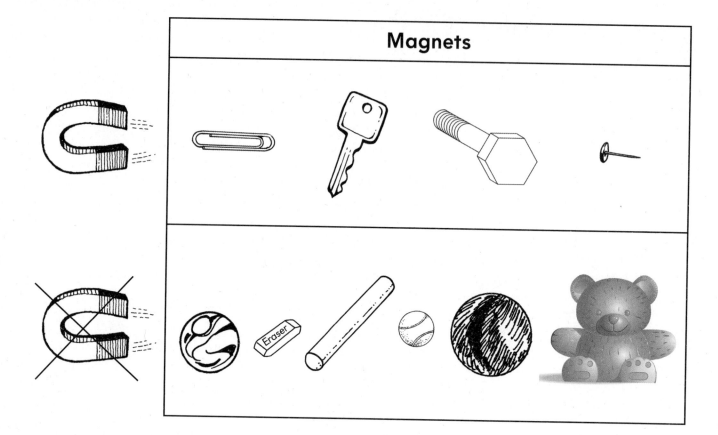

Magnets

_____

- - - - - - - - -

_____

_____

- - - - - - - - -

_____

DIRECTIONS Look at the graph. **2.** How many objects does the magnet attract? Write the number. **3.** How many objects does the magnet not attract? Write the number.

STEM 24

Picture Glossary

above [arriba, encima]

The kite is **above** the rabbit.

add [sumar]

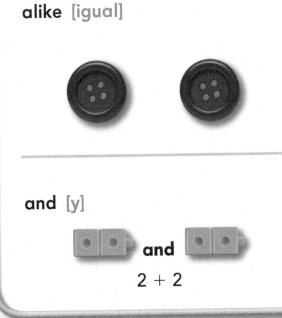

$$3 + 2 = 5$$

alike [igual]

and [y]

and

$$2 + 2$$

behind [detrás]

The box is **behind** the girl.

below [debajo]

The rabbit is **below** the kite.

beside [al lado]

The tree is **beside** the bush.

big [grande]

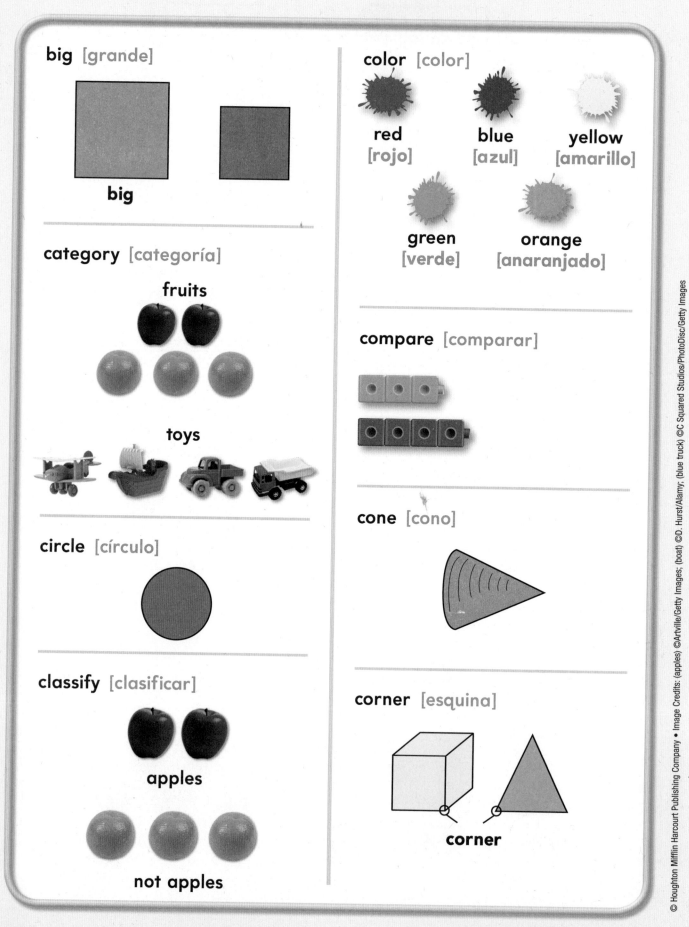

big

category [categoría]

fruits

toys

circle [círculo]

classify [clasificar]

apples

not apples

color [color]

red
[rojo]

blue
[azul]

yellow
[amarillo]

green
[verde]

orange
[anaranjado]

compare [comparar]

cone [cono]

corner [esquina]

corner

cube [cubo]

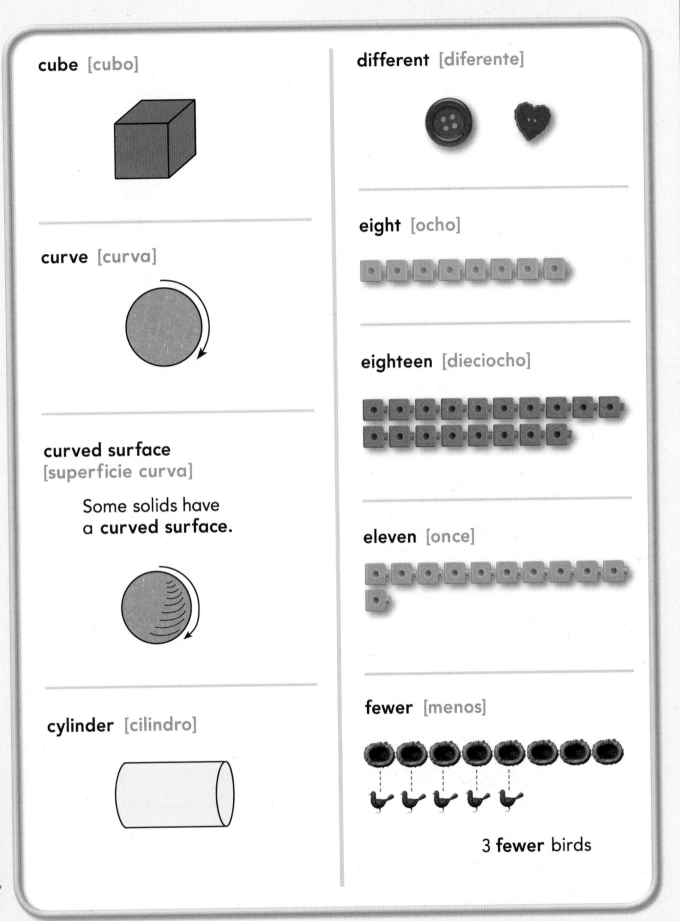

curve [curva]

curved surface
[superficie curva]

Some solids have
a **curved surface**.

cylinder [cilindro]

different [diferente]

eight [ocho]

eighteen [dieciocho]

eleven [once]

fewer [menos]

3 **fewer** birds

fifteen [quince]

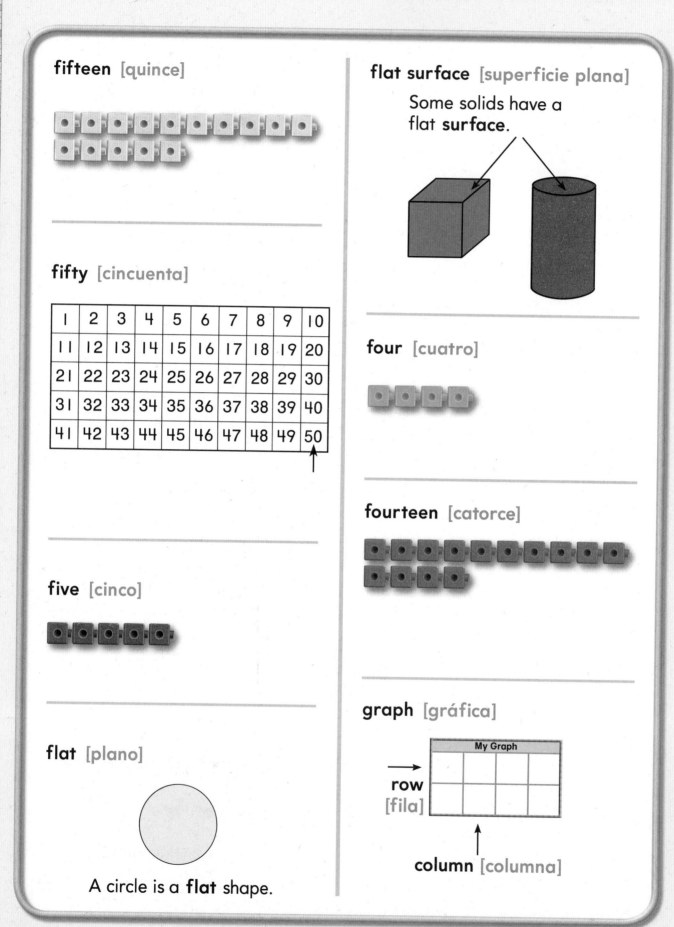

fifty [cincuenta]

1	2	3	4	5	6	7	8	9	10
11	12	13	14	15	16	17	18	19	20
21	22	23	24	25	26	27	28	29	30
31	32	33	34	35	36	37	38	39	40
41	42	43	44	45	46	47	48	49	50

five [cinco]

flat [plano]

A circle is a **flat** shape.

flat surface [superficie plana]

Some solids have a flat **surface**.

four [cuatro]

fourteen [catorce]

graph [gráfica]

My Graph

row [fila]

column [columna]

H4

greater [mayor]

9 is greater than 6

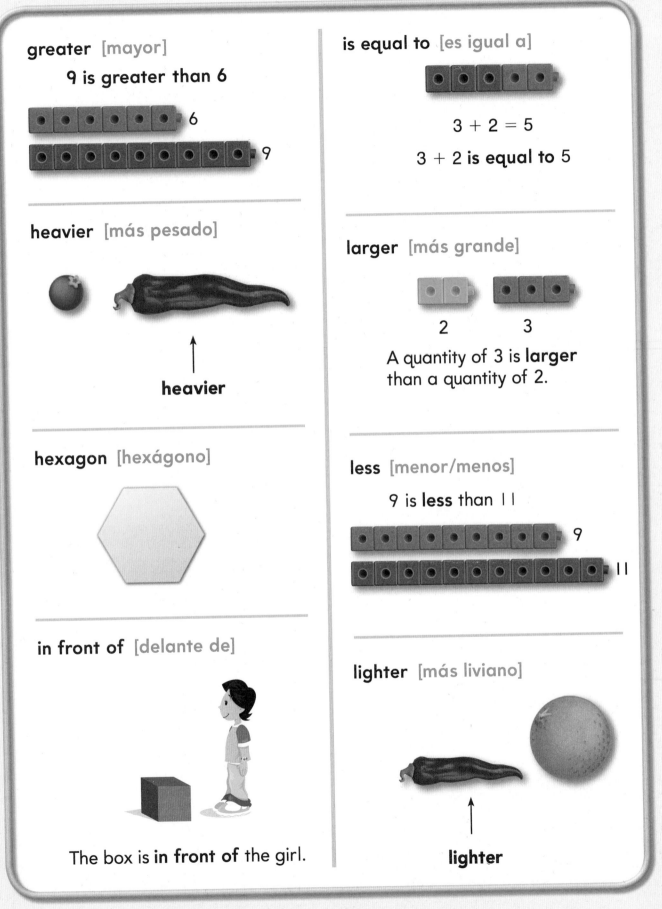

6

9

is equal to [es igual a]

$3 + 2 = 5$

$3 + 2$ **is equal to** 5

heavier [más pesado]

heavier

larger [más grande]

2   3

A quantity of 3 is **larger** than a quantity of 2.

hexagon [hexágono]

less [menor/menos]

9 is less than 11

9

11

in front of [delante de]

The box is **in front of** the girl.

lighter [más liviano]

lighter

longer [más largo]

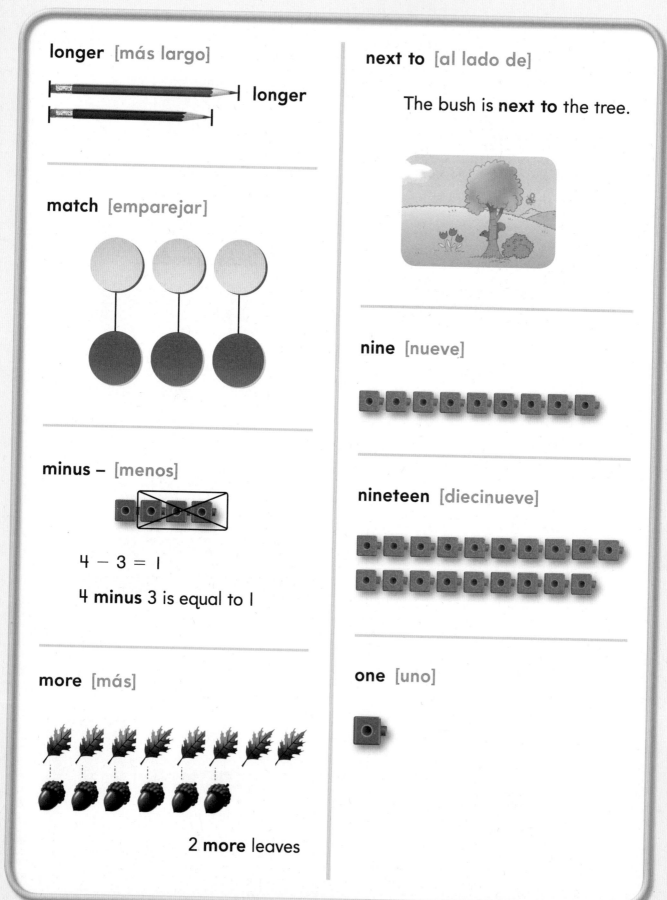

longer

match [emparejar]

minus − [menos]

$4 - 3 = 1$

4 **minus** 3 is equal to 1

more [más]

2 **more** leaves

next to [al lado de]

The bush is **next to** the tree.

nine [nueve]

nineteen [diecinueve]

one [uno]

one hundred [cien]

1	2	3	4	5	6	7	8	9	10
11	12	13	14	15	16	17	18	19	20
21	22	23	24	25	26	27	28	29	30
31	32	33	34	35	36	37	38	39	40
41	42	43	44	45	46	47	48	49	50
51	52	53	54	55	56	57	58	59	60
61	62	63	64	65	66	67	68	69	70
71	72	73	74	75	76	77	78	79	80
81	82	83	84	85	86	87	88	89	90
91	92	93	94	95	96	97	98	99	100

ones [unidades]

3 **ones**

pairs [pares]

3

3	0
2	1
1	2
0	3

number **pairs** for 3

plus + [más]

2 **plus** 1 is equal to 3

$2 + 1 = 3$

rectangle [rectángulo]

roll [rodar]

same height
[de la misma altura]

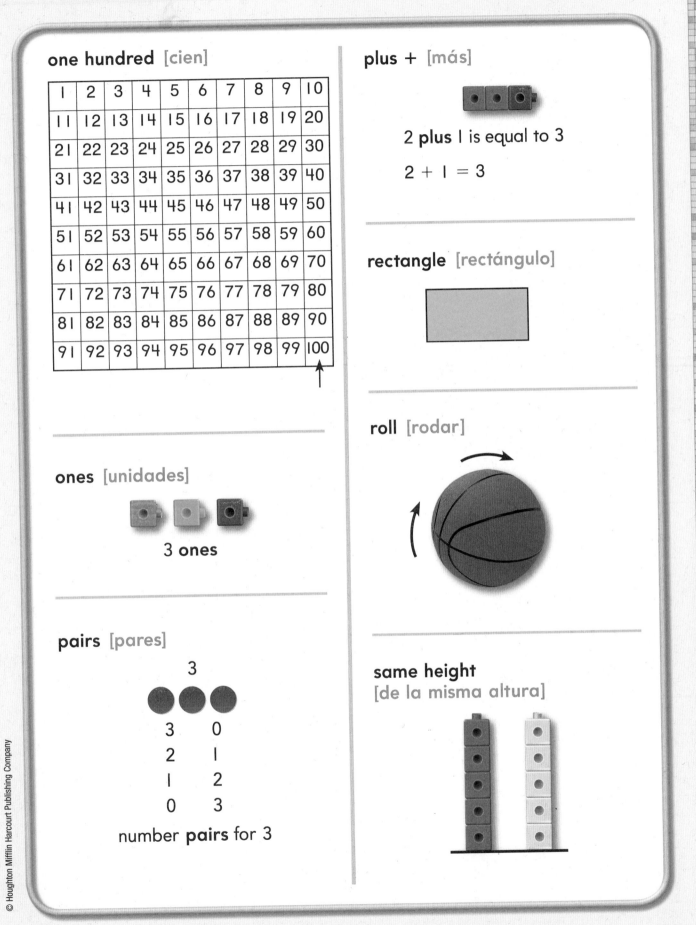

same length [del mismo largo]

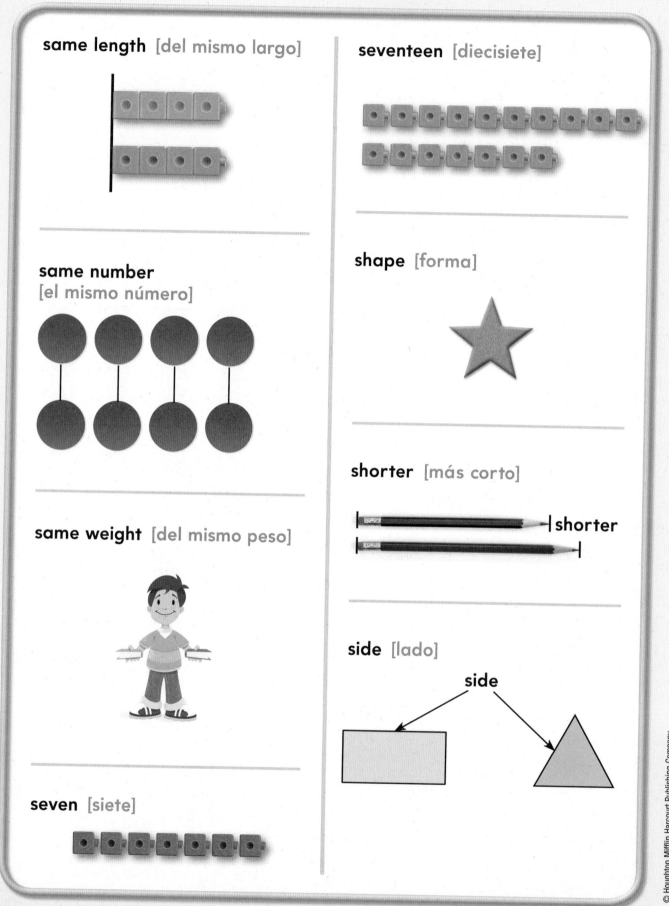

seventeen [diecisiete]

same number
[el mismo número]

shape [forma]

same weight [del mismo peso]

shorter [más corto]

shorter

side [lado]

side

seven [siete]

sides of equal length [lados del mismo largo]

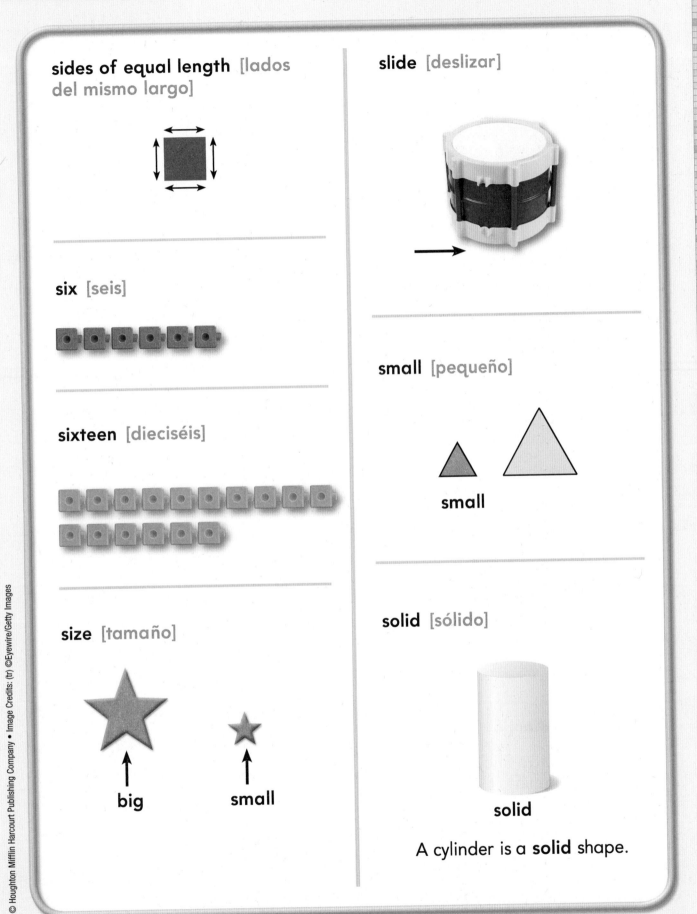

six [seis]

sixteen [dieciséis]

size [tamaño]

big   small

slide [deslizar]

small [pequeño]

small

solid [sólido]

solid

A cylinder is a **solid** shape.

sphere [esfera]

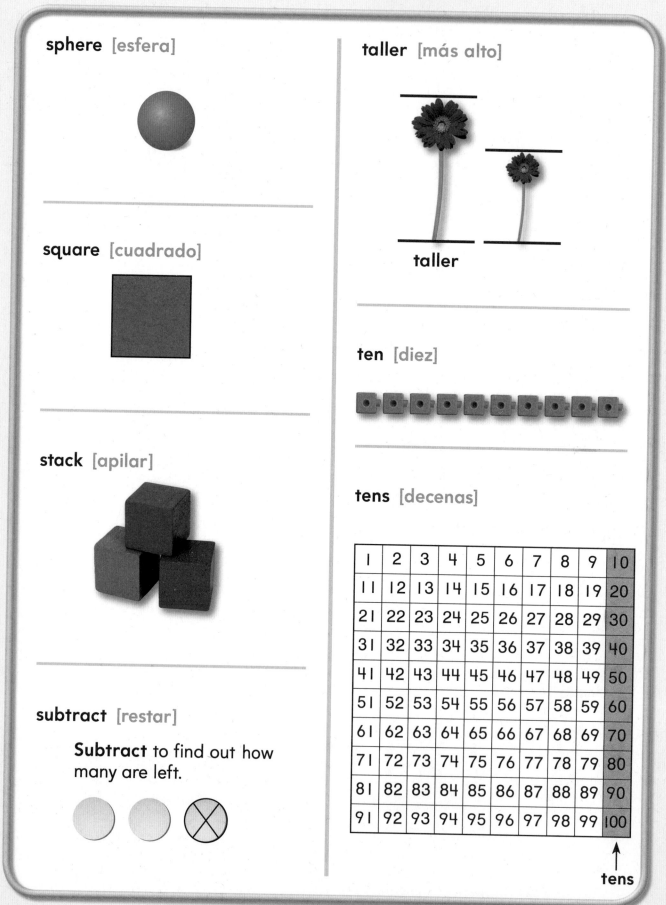

square [cuadrado]

stack [apilar]

subtract [restar]

Subtract to find out how many are left.

taller [más alto]

taller

ten [diez]

tens [decenas]

1	2	3	4	5	6	7	8	9	10
11	12	13	14	15	16	17	18	19	20
21	22	23	24	25	26	27	28	29	30
31	32	33	34	35	36	37	38	39	40
41	42	43	44	45	46	47	48	49	50
51	52	53	54	55	56	57	58	59	60
61	62	63	64	65	66	67	68	69	70
71	72	73	74	75	76	77	78	79	80
81	82	83	84	85	86	87	88	89	90
91	92	93	94	95	96	97	98	99	100

tens

thirteen [trece]

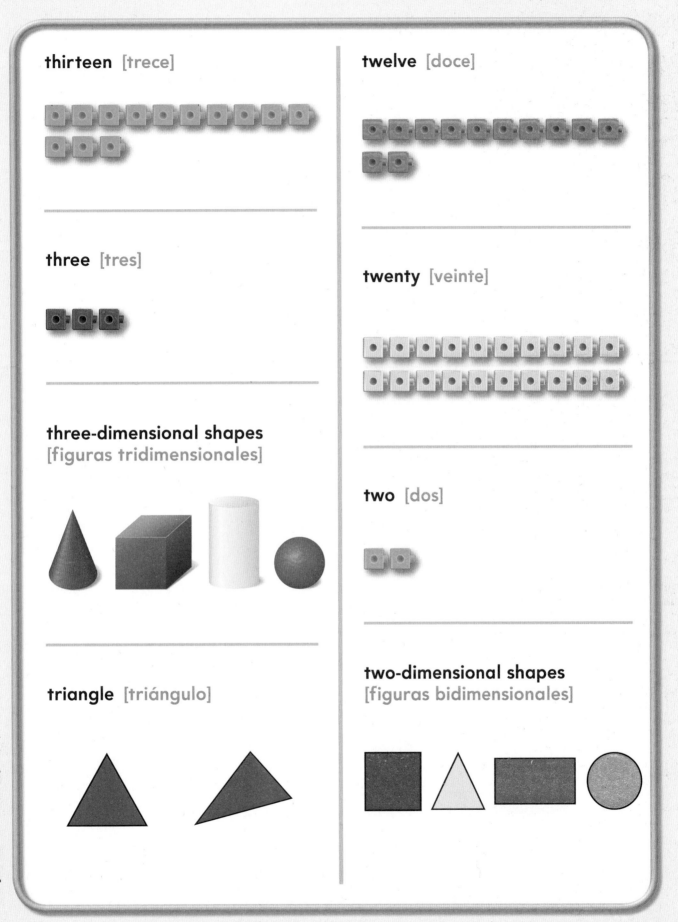

three [tres]

three-dimensional shapes
[figuras tridimensionales]

triangle [triángulo]

twelve [doce]

twenty [veinte]

two [dos]

two-dimensional shapes
[figuras bidimensionales]

vertex [vértice]

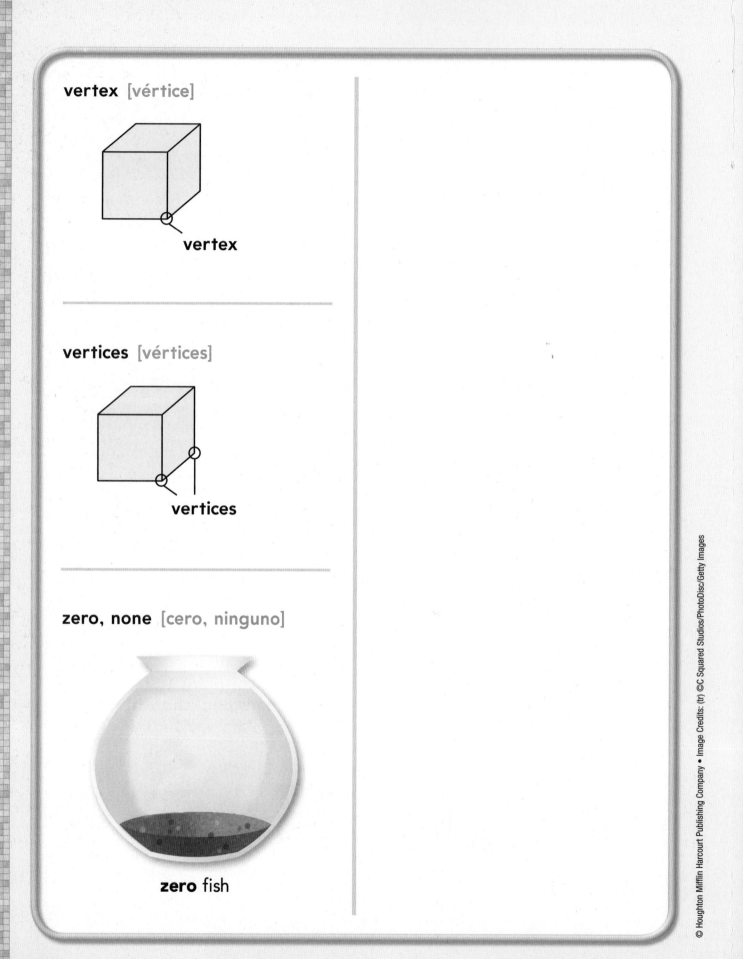

vertex

vertices [vértices]

vertices

zero, none [cero, ninguno]

zero fish

Index

Above, 615–618

Activities
    Games. *See* Games
    Home. *See* Home Activity

Act Out Addition Problems, 243–246

Act Out Subtraction Problems, 323–326

Add
    fluently within 5, 231–234, 243–246,
        249–251, 261–264, 273–276

Addition
    add to, 231–234
    equations, 255–258, 261–264,
        267–270, 273–276, 279–282,
        285–288, 291–294, 297–300
    is equal to, 243–244, 249, 255,
        267–268, 273, 285, 297
    model and draw, 249–251
    number pairs, 273–276, 279–282,
        285–288, 291–294, 297–300
    plus, 237–240, 243–246, 249–251,
        255–258, 261–264, 267–270,
        273–276, 279–282, 285–288,
        291–294, 297–300
    problem solving, act out addition
        problems, 243–246
    put together, 237–240
    sentences, 255–258, 261–264,
        267–270, 273–276, 279–282,
        285–288, 291–294, 297–300
    subtraction and, 347–350
    ways to make ten, 193–196
    word problems, 231–234, 237–240,
        243–246, 249–251, 258, 264, 276,
        282, 288, 294, 300

Add to, 231–234

Algebra
    addition
        model and draw problems, 249–251
        number pairs, 273–276, 279–282,
            285–288, 291–294, 297–300
        sentences, 255–258, 261–264,
            267–270

        subtraction and, 347–350
    classify
        and count by color, 687–690
        and count by shape, 693–696
        and count by size, 699–701
    compare two-dimensional shapes,
        553–556
    subtraction
        addition and, 347–350
        model and draw problems, 329–331
        sentences, 335–338, 341–344
    ways to make 5, 49–52
    ways to make 10, 193–196

Alike, 553–556

Assessment
    Chapter Review/Test, 73–76, 111–114,
        173–176, 223–226, 303–306,
        353–356, 421–424, 477–480,
        565–568, 633–636, 679–682,
        717–720
    Mid-Chapter Checkpoint, 34, 96, 140,
        202, 252, 332, 394, 450, 526, 600,
        664, 702
    Show What You Know, 10, 78, 116,
        178, 228, 308, 358, 426, 490, 570,
        646, 684

Behind, 627–630

Below, 615–618

Beside, 621–624

Big, 699–701

Category, 688–690, 693–696, 699, 701

Chapter Review/Test, 73–76, 111–114,
    173–176, 223–226, 303–306, 353–356,
    421–424, 477–480, 565–568, 633–636,
    679–682, 717–720

Circle
    curve, 499–502
    describe, 499–502
    identify and name, 493–496
    sort, 493–496

Classify
    and count by color, 687–690
    and count by shape, 693–696
    and count by size, 699–701

Color
    sort by, 687–690

Compare
    by counting
        sets to 5, 105–108
        sets to 10, 211–214
    heights, 655–663, 673–676
    lengths, 649–652, 673–676
        by matching
        sets to 5, 99–102
        sets to 10, 205–208
    numbers/sets
        greater, 87–90
        less, 93–95
        same, 81–84
        to five, 99–102, 105–108
        to ten, 205–208, 211–214
        to twenty, 447–449
    two-dimensional shapes, 553–556
    two numbers, 217–220
    weights, 667–670, 673–676

Cone
    curved surface, 597–599
    flat surface, 598
    identify, name, and describe, 597–599
    sort, 597

Corners. *See* Vertices

Count
    compare by, 105–108, 211–214
    forward
        to fifty, 453–456
        to one hundred, 459–462, 465–468, 471–474
        to twenty, 429–432, 435–438, 441–444

    model and, 13–16, 25–28, 37–40, 67–70, 119–122, 131–134, 143–146, 155–158, 181–184, 361–364, 373–376, 385–388, 397–400, 409–412, 429–432
    and write, 19–22, 31–33, 43–46, 67–70, 125–128, 137–139, 149–152, 161–164, 187–190, 367–369, 379–382, 385–388, 403–406, 415–418, 435–438
    numbers. *See* Numbers
    by ones, 453–456, 459–462
    by tens, 465–468, 471–474

Cube
    flat surfaces, 586
    identify, name, and describe, 585–588
    sort, 585–588

Curious George®, Curious About Math, 9, 77, 115, 177, 227, 307, 357, 425, 489, 569, 645, 683

Curve
    of circle, 499–502
    sort by, 553–556

Curved surface, 580, 592, 598

Cylinder
    curved surface, 592
    flat surfaces, 592
    identify, name, and describe, 591–594
    sort, 591–594

Data
    classify and count, 687–690, 693–696, 699–701
    graphs, concrete, 705–708, 711–714

Different, 553–556

E

Eight
    count, 143–146, 149–152
    model, 143–146
    write, 149–152

Eighteen
count, 409–412, 415–418
model, 409–412
write, 415–418

Eleven
count, 361–364, 367–370
model, 361–364
write, 367–370

Equations
addition, 243–246, 249–251, 255–258,
261–264, 267–270, 273, 276,
279–282, 285–288, 291–294,
297–300
subtraction, 323–326, 329–331,
335–338, 341–344

Essential Question. In every Student
Edition lesson. Some examples are: 13,
43, 311, 329, 687, 705

Expressions
addition, 231–234, 237–240
subtraction, 311–314, 317–320

Family Involvement
Family Note. *See* Family Note
Home Activity. *See* Home Activity

Fifteen
count, 385–388
draw a picture, 391–393
model, 385–388
use numbers to, 391–393
write, 385–388

Fifty, 453–456

Five
compare
numbers to, 81–84, 87–90, 93–95,
99–102, 105–108
by counting sets to, 105–108
by matching sets to, 99–102
count, 37–40, 43–46
draw, 37–40, 46
fluently add within, 231–234,
243–246, 249–251, 273–276
fluently subtract within, 311–314,
323–326, 329–331, 335–338
model, 37–40

ways to make, 49–52
write, 43–46

Five frames, 13–15, 25–27, 37–39, 81–82,
87–88, 93–94

Flat, 603–606, 609–612. *See also*
Two-Dimensional Shapes.

Flat surface, 586, 592, 598

Four
count, 25–28, 31–33
draw, 25–28
model, 25–28
write, 31–33

Fourteen
count, 373–376, 379–382
model, 373–376
write, 379–382

Games
At the Farm, 686
Bus Stop, 12
Connecting Cube Challenge, 648
Counting to Blastoff, 80
Follow the Shapes, 572
Number Line Up, 118
Number Picture, 492
Pairs That Make 7, 230
Spin and Count!, 180
Spin for More, 310
Sweet and Sour Path, 360
Who Has More?, 428

Geometry, 481–488 *See* Shapes;
Three-dimensional shapes;
Two-dimensional shapes

Glossary, H1–H12

Graph, concrete, 705–708, 711–714

Greater, 87–90

Guided Practice. *See* Share and Show

Hands On, 13–19, 25–28, 37–40, 49–52,
55–58, 81–84, 87–90, 93–95, 119–122,
131–134, 143–146, 155–158, 181–184,

193–196, 237–240, 249–251, 273–276, 279–282, 285–288, 291–294, 297–300, 317–320, 329–331, 347–350, 361–364, 373–376, 385–388, 397–400, 409–412, 429–432, 553–556, 573–576, 579–582, 585–588, 591–594, 597–599, 609–612, 649–652, 655–658, 667–670, 687–690, 693–696, 699–701, 705–708

Heavier, 667–670

Heights
compare, 655–658, 673–676

Hexagon
identify and name, 541–544
describe, 547–550
sides, 547–550
vertices, 547–550

Home Activity, 16, 22, 28, 33, 40, 46, 52, 58, 64, 70, 84, 90, 95, 102, 108, 122, 128, 134, 139, 146, 152, 158, 164, 170, 184, 190, 196, 201, 208, 214, 220, 234, 240, 246, 258, 264, 270, 276, 282, 288, 294, 300, 314, 320, 326, 331, 338, 344, 350, 364, 370, 376, 382, 388, 393, 400, 406, 412, 418, 432, 438, 444, 449, 456, 462, 468, 474, 496, 502, 508, 514, 520, 525, 532, 538, 544, 550, 556, 562, 576, 582, 588, 594, 599, 606, 612, 618, 624, 630, 652, 658, 663, 670, 676, 690, 696, 701, 708, 714

Hundred
count by ones to, 459–462
count by tens to, 465–468

Hundred chart, 459–462, 465–468

I

In front of, 627–630
Is equal to, 243–248

L

Larger, 55–58
Lengths
compare, 649–652, 673–676
Less, 93–95

Lighter, 667–670
Listen and Draw
activity, 25, 87, 93, 131, 143, 155, 193, 199, 237, 249, 255, 273, 279, 285, 291, 297, 317, 329, 347, 361, 367, 373, 379, 385, 397, 403, 409, 415, 429, 435, 441, 453, 459, 465, 511, 523, 535, 547, 553, 573, 655, 687, 693, 699, 705
Real World, 13, 19, 31, 37, 43, 49, 55, 67, 81, 105, 119, 125, 137, 149, 161, 181, 187, 211, 217, 231, 261, 267, 311, 335, 341, 471, 493, 499, 505, 517, 529, 541, 579, 585, 591, 597, 609, 615, 621, 627, 649, 655, 667, 673

Longer, 649–652

M

Manipulatives and Materials
bead string, 364, 376, 388, 400, 412, 421, 432
cone, 597–600
connecting cubes, 310
counters, two–color, 50–52, 121, 133, 145, 157
Number and Symbol Tiles, 347
three-dimensional shapes, 573–576, 603–606, 609–612
two-dimensional shapes, 553–556, 603–606, 609–612

Matching
compare by, 99–102, 205–208

Math Processes and Practices In many lessons. Some examples are:
1. Problem Solving. In many lessons. Some examples are: 25, 37, 61, 167, 231, 243, 249, 261, 267, 311, 323, 329, 335, 341, 391, 673
2. Abstract and Quantitative Reasoning. In many lessons. Some examples are: 13, 19, 25, 31, 37, 43, 55, 61, 67, 87, 231, 237, 243, 249, 255, 261, 267, 273, 279, 285, 511, 523, 535, 547, 585, 591, 597, 687, 693, 699, 705

© Houghton Mifflin Harcourt Publishing Company

3. Use and Evaluate Logical Reasoning. In many lessons. Some examples are: 81, 87, 93, 99, 105, 167, 361, 373, 397, 409, 447, 609, 621, 627, 649, 655, 661, 667, 673
4. Mathematical Modeling. In many lessons. Some examples are: 49, 61, 99, 119, 167, 181, 193, 205, 237, 243, 249, 317, 323, 329, 391, 447, 541, 603, 615, 621, 627
5. Use Mathematical Tools. In many lessons. Some examples are: 55, 81, 87, 93, 99, 119, 131, 143, 155, 181, 205, 237, 317, 347, 385, 429, 447, 493, 499, 505, 517, 529, 541, 553, 559, 573, 579, 585, 591, 597
6. Use Precise Mathematical Language. In many lessons. Some examples are: 105, 211, 217, 429, 465, 493, 499, 505, 517, 529, 573, 579, 585, 591, 597, 621, 627, 649, 655, 661, 667, 673, 687, 693, 699, 705, 711
7. See Structure. In many lessons. Some examples are: 49, 55, 119, 131, 143, 155, 193, 255, 273, 279, 285, 291, 297, 361, 367, 373, 379, 385, 397, 511, 517, 523, 529, 535, 541, 547, 553, 559, 573, 579, 603
8. Generalize. In many lessons. Some examples are: 131, 143, 155, 205, 211, 217, 255, 347, 367, 379, 403, 415, 453, 459, 465, 471, 511, 523, 535, 547, 553, 559, 609, 705, 711

Math Story, 1–8, 481–488, 637–644

Measurement
heights, compare, 655–658, 637–644
lengths, compare, 649–652, 673–676
weights, compare, 667–670, 673–676

Mid-Chapter Checkpoint, 34, 96, 140, 202, 252, 332, 394, 450, 526, 600, 664, 702

Minus, 311–314, 317–320, 323–326, 329–332, 335–338, 341–344, 347–350

Modeling
addition, 249–251, 273–276, 279–282, 285–288, 291–294, 297–300

numbers. *See* Numbers
put together, 237–240
shapes, 609–612
subtraction, 329–331
take apart, 317–320, 329–331
take from, 311–314, 323–326, 336–338, 341–344

Next to, 621–624

Nine
compare to, 167–170
count, 155–158, 161–164
model, 155–158
write, 161–164

Nineteen
compare, 409–412, 415–418
count, 409–412, 415–418
model, 409–412
write, 415–418

Numbers
compare. *See* Compare
eight, 143–146, 149–152, 285–288
eighteen, 409–412, 415–418
eleven, 361–364, 367–370
fifteen, 385–388, 391–394
fifty, 453–456
five, 37–40, 43–46, 273–276
four, 25–28, 31–33
fourteen, 373–376, 379–382
to nine, 167–170
nine, 155–158, 161–164, 291–294
nineteen, 409–412, 415–418
one, 13–16, 19–22
to one hundred, 459–462, 465–468
order. *See* Order
pairs of, 273–276, 279–282, 285–288, 291–294, 297–300
same, 55–58, 81–84
seven, 131–134, 137–139, 279–282
seventeen, 397–400, 403–406
six, 119–122, 125–128, 279–282
sixteen, 397–400, 403–406

ten, 181–184, 187–190, 199–201,
    205–208, 211–214, 297–300
three, 25–28, 31–33
twelve, 361–364, 367–370
twenty, 429–432, 435–438, 441–444
two, 13–16, 19–22
use to 15, 391–393
ways to make 5, 49–52
ways to make 10, 193–196
write, 19–22, 31–33, 43–46, 67–70,
    125–128, 137–139, 149–152,
    161–164, 187–190, 367–370,
    379–382, 385–388, 403–406,
    415–418, 435–438
zero, 61–64, 67–70

One/Ones
    count, 13–16, 19–22, 361–364
    draw, 13–16, 22
    model, 13–16, 361–364
    write, 19–22
On Your Own. *See* Problem Solving
Order
    numbers
        to five, 55–58
        to ten, 199–202
        to twenty, 441–444

Pair, 49–52
Personal Math Trainer. In all Student
    Edition lessons. Some examples are:
    10, 75, 76, 78, 113, 114, 116, 175, 176,
    178, 225, 226, 228, 304, 305, 308, 353,
    356, 358, 422, 423, 426, 479, 480, 490,
    566, 568, 570, 633, 634, 646, 680, 681,
    684, 718, 719
Picture Glossary. *See* Glossary
Plus, 237–240, 243–246, 249–251,
    255–258, 261–264, 267–270, 273–276,
    279–282, 285–288, 297–300

Position words
    above, 615–618
    behind, 627–630
    below, 615–618
    beside, 621–624
    in front of, 627–630
    next to, 621–624
Practice and Homework. In every
    Student Edition lesson. Some
    examples are: 185–186, 247–248,
    321–322, 445–446, 515–516, 601–602,
    671–672
Problem Solving
    activity, 22, 46, 52, 58, 184, 190, 196,
        270, 344, 350, 462, 468, 496, 502,
        508, 514, 520, 532, 538, 556, 576,
        690, 696, 708
    On Your Own, 64, 170, 208, 562, 606
    Real World activity, 16, 28, 40, 70, 84,
        90, 108, 122, 128, 134, 146, 152,
        158, 164, 214, 220, 234, 240, 258,
        264, 276, 282, 288, 294, 300, 314,
        320, 338, 364, 370, 376, 382, 388,
        400, 406, 412, 418, 432, 438, 444,
        456, 474, 544, 550, 582, 588, 594,
        612, 618, 624, 630, 652, 658, 670,
        676, 714
    Real World On Your Own, 102, 246,
        326
    Real World Unlock the Problem, 61,
        99, 167, 243, 323, 391, 603, 661
    strategies
        act out addition problems, 243–245
        act out subtraction problems,
            323–325
        draw a picture, 167–170, 391–393,
            559–562, 661–663
        make a model, 61–64, 99–102,
            205–208, 447–449
    Unlock the Problem, 205, 447, 559
Put Together, 237–240, 249–251, 255–258

Reading
    numbers. *See* Numbers

Real World
 Listen and Draw, 13, 19, 31, 37, 43, 49,
  55, 67, 81, 105, 119, 125, 137, 149,
  161, 181, 187, 211, 217, 231, 237,
  255, 261, 267, 273, 279, 285, 291,
  297, 311, 317, 335, 341, 453, 471,
  493, 499, 505, 517, 529, 541, 547,
  579, 585, 591, 597, 609, 615, 621,
  627, 649, 655, 667, 673, 705
 On Your Own, 102, 246, 326
 Problem Solving, 16, 28, 40, 70, 84, 90,
  108, 122, 128, 134, 146, 152, 158,
  164, 214, 220, 234, 240, 258, 264,
  276, 282, 288, 294, 300, 314, 320,
  338, 364, 370, 376, 382, 388, 400,
  406, 412, 418, 432, 438, 444, 456,
  474, 544, 550, 582, 588, 594, 612,
  618, 624, 630, 652, 658, 670, 676,
  708, 714
 Unlock the Problem, 61, 99, 167, 243,
  323, 391, 603, 658

Rectangle
 describe, 535–538
 identify and name, 529–532
 sides, 535–538
 sort, 529–532
 vertices, 535–538

Roll, 573–576

Same length, 649–652
Same height, 655–658
Same number, 81–84
Same weight, 667–673
Sentences
 number
  addition, 255–258, 261–264,
   267–270
  subtraction, 335–338, 341–344
Sets
 add to, 231–234
 compare
  fewer, 93–95
  more, 87–90
  same number, 81–84

 put together, 237–240
  take apart, 317–320
  take from, 311–314
Seven
 count, 131–134, 137–139
 model, 131–134
 write, 137–139
Seventeen
 count, 397–400, 403–406
 model, 397–400
 write, 403–406
Shape(s) Three-dimensional
 shapes, 573–612;
 Two-dimensional shapes, 489–564
  combine, 559–562
  flat, 603–606
  model, 609–612
  solid, 603–606
  sort by, 693–696
Share and Show. In every Student
 Edition lesson. Some examples are: 14,
 44, 312, 330, 688, 700, 706
Shorter than, 649–652, 657
Show What You Know, 10, 78, 116, 178,
 228, 308, 358, 426, 490, 570, 646, 684
Sides
 hexagon, 547–550
 number of, 511–514
 rectangle, 535–538
 sides of equal length, 511–514
 square, 511–514
 triangle, 523–525
 sides of equal length, 511–514
 number of, 511–514
Six
 count, 119–122, 125–128
 model, 119–122
 write, 125–128
Sixteen
 count, 397–400, 403–406
 model, 397–400
 write, 403–406
Size
 sort by, 699–701
Slide, 573–576
Small, 699–701

Solid, 603–606, 609–612. *See also* Three-dimensional shapes

Sort
circles, 493–496
by color, 687–690
rectangles, 529–532
by shape, 693–696
by size, 699–701
squares, 505–508
three-dimensional shapes, 603–606
triangles, 517–520
two-dimensional shapes, 553–556, 603–606

Sphere
curved surface, 580
identify, name, and describe, 579–582
sort, 579–580

Square
describe, 511–514
identify and name, 505–508
sides, 511–514
sort, 505–508
vertices, 511–514

Strategies. *See* Problem Solving

Subtract
fluently within 5, 311–314, 323–326, 329–331, 335–338

Subtraction
addition and, 347–350
equations, 335–338, 341–344, 347–350
minus, 317–320, 323–326, 331, 332, 335–338, 341–344, 347–350
model and draw, 329–331
problem solving strategy, act out subtraction problems, 323–326
subtraction sentences, 335–338, 341–344
take apart, 317–320, 329–331
take away, 311–313
take from, 311–314, 323–326, 335–338, 341–344
word problems, 311–314, 317–320, 323–326, 335–338, 341–344, 347–350

Symbols. *See* **Minus,** Plus, Is equal to

T

Take apart, 317–320, 329–331

Take from, 311–314, 323–326, 335–338, 341–344

Taller, 655–656

Ten frames, 119, 132, 144, 156, 181–183, 200–201, 237–239, 317–319, 354, 362–363, 374–375, 385–387, 398–399, 404–405, 410–411, 416–417, 442–443

Ten(s)
compare
by counting sets to ten, 211–214
by matching sets to ten, 205–208
two numbers, 217–220
count, 181–184, 187–190, 199–201, 465–468
to, 199–201
forward to, 199–201
order to, 199–201
model, 181–184
ways to make, 193–196
write, 187–190

Test Prep
Mid-Chapter Checkpoint, 34, 96, 140, 202, 252, 332, 394, 450, 526, 600, 664, 702

Think Smarter. In all Student Edition chapters. Some examples are 34, 96, 140, 202, 252, 332, 394, 450, 526, 600, 664, 702

Think Smarter +. In all Student Edition lessons. Some examples are: 75, 76, 113, 114, 175, 176, 225, 226, 304, 305, 353, 356, 422, 423, 479, 480, 566, 568, 633, 634, 680, 681, 718, 719

Thirteen
count, 373–376, 379–382
model, 373–376
write, 379–382

Three
count, 25–28, 31–33
draw, 25–28
model, 25–28
write, 31–33

Three-dimensional shapes
    cone, 597–599
    cube, 585–588
    cylinder, 591–594
    model, 609–612
    roll, 573–576
    slide, 573–576
    solid, 603–606, 609–612
    sort, 573–576
    sphere, 579–582
    stack, 573–576

Triangle
    combine, 559–560
    describe, 523–525
    identify and name, 517–520
    sides, 523–525
    sort, 517–520
    vertices, 523–525

Try Another Problem, 62, 100, 168, 206, 244, 324, 392, 448, 560, 604, 712

Twelve
    count, 361–364, 367–370
    model, 361–364
    write, 367–370

Twenty
    compare numbers to, 447–449
    count, 429–432, 435–438, 441–444
    model, 429–432
    order, 441–444
    write, 435–438

Two
    count, 13–16, 19–22
    draw, 13–16
    model, 13–16
    write, 19–22

Two-dimensional shapes
    circle, 493–496, 499–502
    combine, 559–562
    flat, 609–612
    hexagon, 541–544, 547–550
    model, 609–612
    rectangle, 529–532, 535–538
    square, 505–508, 511–514
    triangle, 517–520, 523–525

U

Unlock the Problem, 205, 447, 559
    Real World, 61, 99, 167, 243, 323, 391, 603, 623

V

Vertex/Vertices
    hexagon, 547–550
    rectangle, 535–538
    square, 511–514
    triangle, 523–525

Vocabulary
    Builder, 11, 79, 117, 179, 229, 309, 359, 427, 491, 571, 647, 685
    Chapter Vocabulary Cards
    Vocabulary Game

W

Weights
    compare, 667–670, 673–679

Write
    numbers. *See* Numbers
    Write Math. *See* Write Math

Write Math, 16, 22, 28, 40, 46, 52, 58, 64, 70, 84, 90, 102, 108, 122, 128, 134, 146, 152, 158, 164, 170, 184, 190, 196, 208, 214, 220, 234, 240, 246, 258, 264, 270, 276, 282, 288, 294, 300, 314, 320, 326, 338, 344, 350, 364, 370, 376, 382, 388, 400, 406, 412, 418, 432, 438, 444, 456, 474, 496, 502, 508, 514, 520, 532, 538, 544, 550, 556, 562, 576, 582, 588, 594, 606, 612, 618, 624, 630, 652, 658, 670, 676, 690, 696, 708

Z

Zero
    count, 67–70
    draw, 70
    model, 61–64
    write, 67–70